Duncan McLaren's first novel, *Tunnel Vision*, was set in an accountancy firm; its first chapter was published in a short story anthology. His second novel, *Archie van Gogh*, did not interest publishers in the least. His third, *Chinese Illustrations of the Path to Immortality*, was so clearly unpublishable (real, spirited, aesthetic, funny) that he didn't even bother to submit it. This is his fourth book.

PERSONAL
DELIVERY
DUNCAN
McLAREN

Quartet Books

First published by Quartet Books Limited in 1998
A member of the Namara Group
27 Goodge Street
London W1P 2LD

A catalogue record for this book is available from the British Library

ISBN 0 7043 8091 9

Printed and bound in Great Britain by C.P.D. (Wales) Ltd

CONTENTS

SOAP CIRCLE

To the Richard Long exhibition at d'Offay's.

Three stone circles made from blocks of slate have been installed. One can be stood inside; I step into it but don't linger. Another has a perimeter which is several blocks thick and would require a leap to be entered, a leap that would disturb the calm ambience here so I don't make it. The third is entirely infilled, jagged edges pointing upwards, and must be viewed from without. I walk round it, considering the red slate – some edges sliced straight by quarrymen or the artist – before turning to the gallery walls.

Stone circles also appear in most of the half-dozen large, framed photos. I stand in front of a wide, flat New Mexican landscape; a lightly clouded sky over miles of featureless, scrubby desert. The circle of wayside stones in the foreground hardly dominates the scene. Does the presence of stone circles over the gallery floor encourage me to engage more with those the artist has assembled and photographed in New Mexico, Iceland, Australia (a bark circle this one, actually) and Dartmoor? Oh, I think it does.

How would I have gone about making this New Mexican stone circle? I'd have reassured myself about the water/sun/temperature situation before getting involved... I'd have established that there were enough loose stones of a suitable size lying around... I'd have marked the centrepoint of the circle to be, and collected a few stones together... I'd have paced out maybe eight radials and placed a stone at the end of each one... I'd have completed the circle by making as few, short trips for stones as possible... And then I'd have made the most of my handiwork in whatever way came to mind at the time. Before contemplating the wider view, taking the photo and being on my way...

As well as photos there are a number of large, framed texts on the walls. Including this:

DUSTLINES
KICKING UP A LINE OF DUST EACH DAY ALONG THE WALKING LINE
A 7 DAY WALK ON THE EAST BANK OF THE RIO GRANDE
EL CAMINO REAL NEW MEXICO 1995

The text doesn't tell me whether the trek was to the north or south, unless 'EL CAMINO REAL' somehow gives that information. In this year's other walks, the artist specifies which way he was going: from the south to the north of Ireland; east from the mouth of the Loire. In New Mexico, perhaps he walked in one direction for a few days then retraced his steps... but this takes me nowhere.

I'd also like to know in which season the walk took place. I suppose the landscape picture gives clues but I don't know enough about desert plants' annual cycle to make use of them... Presumably the walk came after the All Ireland winter walk, but did it come before or after the French walk?

2

Another thing – mileage. France: 121 miles in three and a half days; Ireland 382 miles in twelve days. Very good going – more than thirty miles a day. But last year's progress across the middle of Iceland was slower – 220 miles in fourteen days is only an average of fifteen per day. How fast did he get through New Mexico? – the exhibition doesn't say.

I ask the young woman at the desk about this walk. But she knows no more about it. I ask her about the personality of the artist. All she can say is that at the private view he came across as quiet and self-contained. She asks why I want to know. I shrug and say something about writing.

We talk about the other artists I've written about so far, the stances I've taken and the slim prospects of the material being published. She discloses that she once wrote a romantic novel, but, although she felt she'd followed all the rules of the genre, the book wasn't accepted by Mills and Boon – the only feasible outlet for it – and so that was that. She goes on to say that she still writes, that she's been offered a job by *Sight and Sound* to write film reviews and other articles, and that she's really excited by the prospect. We smile at each other.

I walk once more round the stone circles on the varnished wooden floor of the gallery and, smiling again, go on my way.

•

On to Saatchi's, where Young British Artists are showing.

Soaps and washroom fittings dominate the list of Hadrian Pigott's exhibits. As I cross the huge, white space towards rounded, white shapes, perfume pervades the air.

I veer towards what appears to be an open travelling case. Closer and from a different angle it seems to be the case for a bulky wind instrument. But as I look down into the velvet-lined interior I see a hand-basin complete with taps, plughole and plug. Also set in the velvet are a bar of soap and plumbing components which could, I presume, enable the wash-basin to be plumbed in. Did Richard Long saddle himself with such luggage on his New Mexican trek? Certainly it would explain embarrassingly slow progress across the desert.

My eye is drawn to a group of three round, white boulders. One of them has two taps at the top of it, and is, I now smell, a huge soap. I suppose the boulder shape reflects – materializes – the interior of a sink. Anyway, there is also a plug on a chain resting on the soap boulder, and a plughole between the taps. If the taps were turned on, some of the water from them would go down the plughole into the soap, but most of it would spill down the sides of the boulder. Of course, you no more get water from taps set in a soap boulder than you get blood from a stone. Unless your name is Long, you're in the middle of the New Mexican desert and you're hallucinating

I look towards what turns out to be a row of pristine white bars of soap, equally spaced, each resting on a white, plaster soapdish set into the wall at about waist height. Each soap has a word stamped into it, but not a manufacturer's name. I walk along the row, reading: FEET, LEGS, ARMS, SHOULDERS, NECK, EARS, CHIN, CHEEKS, NOSE, FOREHEAD, HANDS... I stop at HANDS.

I'm aware again of what I'd forgotten about on entering the building. After eating a bag of chips for lunch, my hands reek of vinegar and could do with a wash. I walk away from the display soaps 'n' sinks towards a washroom proper, where I give my hands a good seeing-to with an almost new cake of white soap.

Back in the gallery, a second glance at the list of exhibits tells me that the eighteen soaps refer to the artist's order of washing himself in London on 23 March 1994. I'm now doubting if I went along the row in the right direction. Sure enough, the reverse order makes more sense, given the effect of gravity on soapy water. So: ARMPITS, CHEST, BELLY, PRICK, BALLS, ARSE, BACK, HANDS... I stop at HANDS as before, puzzled.

I can still smell vinegar. I raise my left hand to my nose and confirm the scent of acetic acid. How come?... I suppose the handle of my bag and the pocket of my jacket were contaminated by the vinegar before I washed my hands, and that contact with handle and pocket subsequent to the wash has... oh, it's obvious enough. So what I have to do now is return to the loo and soap my hands again, as well as washing the tainted parts of jacket and bag. Wrong. After all, I haven't been kicking up dust for a week along the Rio Grande; I am relatively clean and the best thing would be simply to move on to a different part of the building and another artist altogether.

Kerry Stewart's *Sleeping Nun* has a room to herself. I try not to feel like an intruder as I approach the figure. She is made of plaster, I think, which has been painted – flesh colour for face and hands, white for the headdress, but mostly black. She is lying on her right side and her front, with her habited head resting on her right wrist and her left forearm stretched out with its palm flat against the floor. Her eyes are shut, her expression...difficult to read.

I back away from the sleeper and sit in a corner of the room. But from here the figure is entirely black, so I slide along the floor until I have sight of pink and white as well. The still predominantly black figure seems to hover above the grey floor. I lean my back against the wall, close my eyes in sympathy with my room-mate...and visualize each stage of my journey home.

•

Home, I step on to a cold bath and under a hot shower. It's not hot yet though.

I imagine a wide, flat landscape with a stone circle in the foreground. Iceland. Inside the circle lies a sleeping nun. The circle is made out of little soaps with words such as... No, the circle is formed by blocks of ice, the nearest of which has 'SLIP IT TO ME' written on it... No, the ice-blocks are wordless, but are moulded into bathroom forms: a sink, a cistern, a lavatory pan... Nonsense, the ice blocks are rocks, smoothed-down limestone perhaps, white and slippery to step on, but warm now.

Hot water pours on to the nape of my neck. Another wide-open landscape, a New Mexican stone circle. In the circle is the girl from d'Offay's. She is sitting at her desk... no, she is sitting at the piano I recognize from my first visit to the gallery, years ago. Joseph Beuys installed the piano and lined the walls of the space with felt. Indeed, I now see that the circle is made out of rolls of felt, standing tall, roll to roll, blocking out my view of the woman...

My hand passes through steam and picks up the nearly new bar of orange soap. I turn it around in my hands. I keep turning it and see that by moving my thumbs I can rotate the soap on its long axis, at speed. The soap spins round in my hands, lathering up. What do I do with all this liquid soap? I put the bar back on its dish, stick my right hand in my left oxter and my left hand in my right oxter, and rub away. Soap overflows from my armpits and I smooth it over my chest and belly. Am I going to wash in Pigott order, then? Certainly I have started that way and will finish with my feet for practical reasons – the slipperiness of this bath. I carry on with my ablutions.

I could have said much more to the woman at d'Offay's. She told me that *Sight and Sound* intends to give space in their review section to avant-garde films and videos. And I did recommend *Humiliate* by Bob and Roberta Smith, which she took a note of. But I didn't give her an idea of what that work was really like, even though I could very easily have done so. My prick is clean.

Also, I mentioned to her that I'd been to the Richard Long show held at d'Offay's a couple of years back. But I didn't go on to say that I'd been stimulated by it into making a walk of my own. I remember the event well, and how I commemorated it:

THE RIDGEWAY

ROADS PATHS AND ANCIENT TRACKWAYS FROM GORING TO PRINCES RISBOROUGH

A 25 MILE NIGHT WALK WITH JOANNA

FULL MOON 4-5 JULY 1993

My balls are...

WALK OF THREE STOPS

A STOP UNDER A RAILWAY BRIDGE FOR A MIDNIGHT FEAST

A STOP AT CART GAP THROUGH GRIMS DITCH FOR REST AT 2 A.M.

(THE EARTH MIGHT BE UNINHABITED)

A STOP AT NUFFIELD CHURCH FOR WATER AT DAWN

CHILTERNS

SUMMER 1993

My balls are clean. My arse and hands too. The soap is spinning round in my hands again. I use the tips of fingers of both hands to rub soap into my forehead. I slowly pull my hands down over my face – two fingers sliding down each side of my nose, the heel of my thumb slipping over my cheeks. I use the tip of my right index finger alone to rub soap into my chin but change to the middle fingers of both hands to clean my ears.

Soap circle; neck. I place my left hand on the back of my neck above where the right hand lies. I make little circling movements of both hands, then alter the action so hands are encircling back and sides of the cylinder. Letting go, I clasp myself around the throat, right-handed, and slide my hand up and down until all the soap has gone. I place the tips of my fingers at the base of my skull and draw them down over the back of my neck to the tops of my shoulders, flesh squeaking. My neck has never felt cleaner.

I suddenly realize that the whole tenor of today has been set by a couple of things that happened yesterday. Seeing Gilbert and George's 'Naked Shit' pictures at the South London Gallery. And, more important, meeting Joanna in the evening and parting from her by mutual consent until the second week in December – a trial separation. I wash on...

Both my feet have been lathered and rinsed. I help the last soapsuds down the plughole. Am I disposing of all traces of my lover? I don't see it that way. Rather, I am cleaning up my act for when we get together again.

I hope I'm doing the right thing. I hope I'm doing the right thing but fear I may be overdoing it:

Two nuns in a bath.
First Nun: 'Where's the soap?'
Second Nun: 'It certainly does.'

SOAP CIRCLE

ARMPITS

CHEST

BELLY

PRICK

BALLS

ARSE

BACK

HANDS

FOREHEAD

NOSE

CHEEKS

CHIN

EARS

NECK

SHOULDERS

ARMS

LEGS

FEET

A HALF-HOUR SHOWER TOWARDS THE END OF THE AFTERNOON
FOREST HILL   SEPTEMBER 28 1995

JOANNA

SHOWER CURTAIN

ARMPITS

BREASTS

BELLY

PUBES

CUNT

ARSE

BACK

HANDS

FOREHEAD

NOSE

CHEEKS

CHIN

EARS

NECK

SHOULDERS

ARMS

LEGS

FEET

IN ANTICIPATION

HANDS

MAYBE NOT

To the Serpentine Gallery, where actress Tilda Swinton is sleeping in a glass case for eight hours a day all this week.

The case is raised above waist height. She is lying there, sleeping on her left side, wearing casual clothes and a watch, with her glasses beside her on the mattress and a supply of water to hand. Her red hair has been wound into a pile on top of her head, but long streams of it are cascading over the white cotton pillowcase. It seems she is asleep: her eyes are still behind the lids and there is a sheen to the skin of her face. Thirty pairs of strangers' eyes, mine included, bear down on this vulnerable individual.

I walk round the rest of the gallery, where other raised cases installed by Cornelia Parker contain exhibits relating to famous dead people, but soon I return to the main attraction. She has turned on to her right side, seducing her audience into the narrower space between the case and the north wall. Her closed left eye – the one clear of the pillow – is the focus of interest. The smooth curves of the delicate skin between eyebrow and eyelashes are not interrupted by the sharp creases that usually define the upper course of the eye. I don't think she is asleep now judging by a tremble of eyelid.

'God, she's ugly!' says a voice from alongside, startling me. It doesn't visibly disturb the sleeper, though if she is awake she certainly heard that. I stare at the speaker. He confidently meets my gaze – clearly, fully expecting me to agree with his observation.

I linger, my attention divided between the sleeping beauty and the other. I see him lying on the rug from Freud's analyst's couch, I see him lying there wearing Arthur Askey's suit, clutching to his chest Scott of the Antarctic's pathetic bag of last provisions. And I see him – diagnosed untreatably insane – stumbling out of the building, with Churchill's king-sized cigar protruding from his fast-disappearing arse.

She sleeps on in tranquillity.

THE Beatles

QUIZ

1. WHICH BEATLE WAS BORN IN DETROIT NOT MANCHESTER ?

   ....

2. WHO SHOT GEORGE ?

   ....

3. WHEN WAS THE BEATLES SINGLE HEY LUCIANA RELEASED ?

   ....

4. WHEN DID THE BEATLES REFORM ?

   ....

5. WHO REPLACED GEORGE ON DRUMS ?

   ....

6. WHERE WAS PAUL AND YOKO'S WEDDING ?

   ....

7. WHO IS MARRIED TO BRIAN EPSTEIN ?

   ....

8. JOHN AND RINGO WROTE MOST OF THE SONGS BUT WHO WROTE CATCH US IF YOU CAN

   ....

9. WHERE DO JOHN AND LINDA LIVE NOW ?

   ....

10. WHICH BEATLE HAS A HEART BYPASS ?

    ....

The following Beatles Quiz is based on the above Beatles Quiz by Bob and Roberta Smith.

THE **Beatles** QUIZ

1 Which Beatle flew to the Algarve this year for his summer holidays?

2 Which Beatle paid for the flight in advance (£119), paid for a hire car in advance (£119), but decided to find accommodation when he got out there?

3 Which Beatle's partner had to do all the talking (French and Portuguese) when it came to booking a hotel room in Loule?

4 Which Beatle was able to stop the washroom door (which would lock from the inside but wouldn't otherwise shut) banging at night, by judicious positioning of toilet rolls fore and aft, but was unable to do anything about the creaking of their room's window's shutters – also caused by the constant veering of the wind through 180 degrees?

(Closing the shutters was not an option as the temperature of the room rapidly rose to an uncomfortable level.)

5   Which Beatle used the bidet three times a day but still couldn't hear his arse squeaking as he walked down the street for the sound of Portuguese arses squeaking?

6   Which Beatle enjoyed quiet walks with his companion along dry valleys, over rocky hillsides and amongst the exotic trees – fig, olive, eucalyptus, carob and cork oak – of the limestone and shale areas of the Algarve, always mindful of the power of the midday sun? (He would be looking more closely at ash, apple, sycamore, rowan and English oak when he got back home: all trees are fruit trees.)

7   Which Beatle decided to hire the car for a second week (now that his driver had found reverse gear), but on learning that this would cost 40,000 *escudos* (£159) locally, spent a couple of hours making calls to the UK (cost £10) in order to secure the yellow Twingo at the same price as before?

8   Which Beatle's partner explained that cork oaks are harvested every nine years – the bark is stripped off the trunk all the way round for several feet up the tree and a number is painted on the exposed trunk to indicate the year of harvest – and led them to the village football pitch which served as the cork collection centre, where enormous piles of bark were drying out?

9   Which Beatle took a series of photos of cork oaks harvested this year?

10 Which Beatle organized a 'stroll through time' by following the trail the cork harvesters had made through the jungle of gum cistus, observing that when newly stripped the underlying trunk is brilliant orange (5), which changes to a dark orange (4), then reddish brown (3), then brown (2), eventually darkening (1) to a grey-brown (0) and (9) finally (8) to grey (7) black (6)?

11 Which Beatle's companion realized that they'd walked for six hours; that it was still extremely hot; that while they couldn't be far from the village to which their circular route led, they'd come to a cork oak not harvested since 1986 which had only one path leading from it – the overgrown trail by which they'd got there; and, furthermore, that her partner had forgotten the reserve water bottle? (Oh, Christ!)

12 Which Beatle had to lie down in the shady clearing underneath the cork oak because he suddenly felt blood pounding in his head?

13 Which Beatle, feeling really weird, said, 'We want to be free...to do what we want to do...'?

14 Which Beatle, prostrate, couldn't get 'Yellow Submarine' out of his mind? (Verse, chorus; words and tune; on and on and on.)

15 Which Beatle, in order to get 'Yellow Submarine' out of his mind, sang a medley of Beatles hits which he introduced as a 'stroll down memory lane' and which included 'Help', 'Norwegian Wood', 'Let It Be', 'She's Leaving Home', 'Lovely Rita', 'Paint It Black', 'Sunny Afternoon', 'Happy Xmas –

War is Over', 'Good Vibrations', 'My Sweet Lord', 'Horse with No Name', 'When I'm 64', 'Chirpy-Chirpy Cheep-Cheep', 'When I'm 64' (reprise), 'Mama, We're All Crazy Now', 'Paperback Writer', 'Nowhere Man', 'Hey Jude', 'Fool on the Hill', 'Yesterday', 'Imagine', 'Yesterday'...?

16 Which Beatle's companion drew the line at a maudlin, extended-mix, hard-hands version of 'The Long and Winding Road'?

17 Which Beatle, feeling vaguely normal again but with a dehydration headache raging, said, 'We've got to think about our situation... And make a half-ways sensible decision about what to do next.'?

18 Which Beatle took a photo of his lover at the end of the walk, and laughed with her about the whole adventure over their sardines and vinho verde (reconstituted cork, alas) that night?

19 Which Beatle discovered his partner in tears three times during the holiday?

20 Which Beatle landed at Gatwick with the same five words of Portuguese that he'd taken off with?

21 NAME THAT BEATLE.

The Pledge of Fidelity,
The Pledge of Self-Discipline

Wednesday, 1 November

Letter from Joanna. It tells me she has been using our trial separation as a chance to get some kind of realistic perspective on our relationship and to focus on what seem to be the key issues from, she thinks, both our points of view. Wrote back to say that I was off to see an installation by this woman who'd been wearing a chastity belt recently.

Thursday, 2 November

Entered a dark space where there were three video monitors showing a woman in various degrees of nakedness. The contraption around her thighs concentrated my attention and my eyes flicked from screen to screen in an effort to build a clear picture of the metal-bound flesh. Until I realized that the female invigilator who had followed me into the room was standing behind me, possibly following my line of vision, my train of thought. Exit in confusion.

Friday, 3 November

Re-entered exhibition in more steadfast mood. To begin with my eyes flicked back and forth again. Soon I settled to watch the tape-loops in their entirety. The shortest (middle monitor, about three minutes) showed the artist, Louisa, taking a piss despite her chastity belt. The longest (right monitor, maybe twenty minutes) showed her having a bath in the device. The third screen showed the woman using pads and creams to make herself comfortable in the metal contraption. Now and again a line of text would appear briefly on a screen, such as, 'There are so many things that I no longer take for granted.' Also there was a soundtrack, about as long as the bathing scene but not synchronized with it, of Louisa describing her thoughts and feelings while wearing the belt.

As I walked out after more than an hour in the darkened room, I thanked the invigilator – who smiled back easily enough, despite having been kept away from her psychology book for so long.

Saturday, 4 November

Re-entered exhibition space from which the installation had been removed, and where Louisa MacIver, her collaborator Karen F, and two critics were to talk about the show. The discussion was fascinating, so it seemed a pity there were only about a dozen of us in the audience. Apparently this was to do with lack of publicity. The show was first presented in Hull, where it was promoted using an image of Louisa in the chastity belt, leading to feminist protests and unfortunate features in the popular press. 'Lovely Louisa, 26... '

Louisa described the device for those who hadn't seen the installation. A metal belt encircled her waist; a metal plate passed down over her fanny then bent under her pubic bone and stopped just short of her anus; two chains linked to the end of the metal plate passed up her crack, separated in a V at the top of her buttocks and attached to the metal belt behind her.

The matter of the key-holder was raised. Louisa's boyfriend had agreed (reluctantly – it put him in an invidious position) to keep the key. Louisa wore the belt for over two months, except when it was removed by him for sex. I asked Louisa if she had considered being her own key-holder, but did so in too self-conscious a way to effectively follow up the answer, which was 'Yes.' It was an ill-considered question anyway – presumably she wanted to know what it was like to wear a chastity belt psychologically as well as physically.

Monday, 6 November

At my table I started this diary, wrote it up to date and stared at the key to my room which was in its usual place – sticking out from the keyhole on the inside of the door. I put down my pen, walked to the door, took hold of the cold metal key between forefinger and thumb and tried to turn it. The strain was greatest on my thumb, though some of it went up wrist, through elbow, to upper arm, before the key turned with a crunch. I pulled the key out of the lock, crouched down and gazed through the keyhole... but I couldn't make much out of what I saw. So I slipped the key back in place, felt pressure against the side of my index finger and felt strain dissolve right up my arm as the mechanism suddenly released and the key turned. Back at the table I write this diary entry, intending to go on and draft descriptions of the videos of Louisa filmed by Karen F.

The camera looks down from above the door into a small loo. Louisa enters the room, pulls down her leggings, her tights and her knickers, and sits on the toilet seat. She removes a wad of padding from either side of the chastity belt's metal frontpiece and, bending forward, places them on the floor in front of her, briefly revealing her chained bottom to the camera's high vantage. She puts her left hand behind her back, presumably to hold the chains in some way as she urinates. Then she uses her left hand to pull out a tissue from a box and wipe herself from the rear. A second tissue she uses at her front. With a third she thoroughly wipes the metal frontpiece before dabbing to her rear again. As she leans forward to pick up the wads of padding, her buttocks are exposed as before. She carefully replaces the pads either side of her pubic area. She stands, pulls up her knickers, tights and leggings, flushes the toilet and exits the room.

Accurate? I think so, I made notes at the time. Next...

The camera looks across at the bath from the doorway. Louisa enters the room, discards jeans, shirt and bra, and steps into the bathwater. She lies down in the bath, only the left side of her face and head visible. Eventually she sits up and takes hold of the soap. She washes her shoulders, breasts, neck and back before lying back down in the water. A little later she kneels, picks up the soap again and washes her hips. She stands up in order to soap her buttocks, and the chains that divide them, and her crack, and the underside of the metal belt round her waist. She remains standing, knees flexed now, as she thoroughly soaps her pubic area. She lies down in the bath to rinse off, and then lies still for a while. When she next sits up it is to wash her feet, then to soap her forehead, nose, cheeks and chin. She rinses clear, then goes on stroking her face, ending up by passing her fingers through her hair from the top of her forehead to the nape of her neck several times. She lies back in the water once more, for a long soak. In due course she stands, steps out of the bath, dries herself and her chastity belt, slips into a dressing gown, which she ties at the waist, and exits the room.

Fine. Though I can't really remember the relative lengths of each lie-back. When not much was happening I could be distracted by the soundtrack or by another screen...

The camera looks across at a long mirror standing in the corner of a bathroom. Louisa enters the room in bra and panties and stands in the right foreground of the frame with her back to the lens. Her front is visible in the mirror. She takes some cream from a jar to her right and rubs it along the inside of the metal waistband throughout its circumference. She slips her panties down to her knees and applies cream to her bottom, kneading her buttocks, and then to the chains, her hands passing up and down each one. She takes a length of padded material, folds it over the belt so that it hangs between the belt and her side, sprinkles talcum powder on to the pad and repeats these steps with a pad at her other side. She removes wads of cotton wool from behind the frontpiece, wipes her crotch, applies both cream and talcum powder to it, flicks her hand several times against her knickers and inserts a fresh pad of cotton wool either side of her pubic area. She pulls up her panties, inspects her appearance in the mirror, turns round, looks over first one shoulder then the other while adjusting the lie of her knickers, and then exits the room.

My notes aren't so complete on this one, which may well be inaccurate. I didn't really understand what she was doing and this must have stopped me from simply looking. Simply looking...

Tuesday, 7 November

Copied video résumés into diary then produced sketch from memory. The perspective isn't right – it looks like she's squatting over the toilet rather than sitting on the seat – and I've surely exaggerated the length of her thighs, but it'll do.

Failed to ignore the key.

Wednesday, 8 November

Failed to ignore the key.

Thursday, 9 November

Failed (comprehensively) to ignore the key.

Friday, 10 November

Failed to ignore the key. Better come clean over this sexual fantasy business. Here is the gist:

I approach Louisa, who is in her bathroom and naked except for chastity belt. I instruct her to kneel down and bend over. I put the head of the long key into the lock and turn the mechanism with an emphatic clunk. The contraption slides off her body. I turn her around, spread her legs and – without hesitation or consideration, but with anticipation, eagerness – thrust my quivering erection up her cunt. Gratification comes quickly...

Oh dear. Is this rape? Louisa doesn't consent to the sex, that's for sure. On the other hand, she has set herself up somewhat.

I have just succeeded – just – in ignoring the key. So let's ensure that's that – I really must move on from here.

Saturday, 18 November

Met Joanna at the Royal Festival Hall. It was good to see her – very arousing. She asked me to look at the artists' books on display, so I did, but couldn't get into them, and I doubt if I'll be applying to do the M.A. in Book Arts at Camberwell as she suggests. But the real purpose of meeting was to discuss our relationship. She elaborated on her written comment that – because she felt shut out by me – she'd effectively withdrawn from me sexually and emotionally over a year ago. We spent the afternoon talking round and through this. And we confirmed we would spend the second weekend of December together unless circumstances changed for either of us.

Sunday, 19 November

Went walking. The streets of London are paved with leaves newly fallen from plane trees. Great pieces of parchment some of them. One leaf would have stretched beyond the edges of an A3 sheet. I nearly took it home with me.

Monday, 20 November

Decided to have another go at a diary. I went to Smith's, assessed the options and bought an A4-sized book with hard black covers and plain white pages. At my table I opened the book and used a Stanley knife together with a steel rule to cut out a narrow oblong across the top of the first page through all the pages. Then I taped the key to the door of my room on to the inside of the back cover in the middle of the oblong window. I kept opening the book, flicking through and closing it again. It felt right, but I thought I'd sleep on it before doing anything drastic.

Tuesday, 21 November

Copied entries from the old diary into this one then wrote up the last three days. Didn't take as long as it might and gave me a chance to edit down. Now I am sitting at table in the early evening trying to remember what Louisa said on the installation soundtrack. Her oral diary...

She talked about the struggle she had with the chastity belt. It was too tight at times; it rubbed against her in certain places. She bought rolls of cotton wool and various types of pad to try to stop the skin breaking. She used talcum powder, which made the skin scab before it bled, which was, she felt, preferable.

She tried to forget about the belt but often this was difficult. She'd get depressed around eight in the evening, knowing that she was going to feel increasingly uncomfortable until morning. Sunday night was particularly bad. Other people would be relaxing in the flat – watching TV or drinking wine – and she'd get irritable. Which was out of character for her, and upsetting.

By midnight the belt felt hot. She could make out its shape in heat, especially the waistband. She slept badly. The metal front-piece was tight against her fanny bone and she was bruised down there. Also her pubic hair became caught in the device, creating an itch. Indeed sleeping was the worst part of it.

Perhaps not the worst part. She said that she'd gone four or five days without her bowels moving. With food going in and nothing coming out, the belt got tighter and tighter. But the tension and the tightness made it hard to shit until she really had to.

Water helped her to forget about the belt. A shower felt good; the water and then the redressing soothed her body. But a bath was better. She put witch hazel in the bathwater for its healing qualities, and she lay there for ages. She'd never been keen on long baths but this had converted her. She couldn't feel a thing while she lay there. No metal constraining her body. Wonderful.

She talked about the removal of the device. That she wanted him to do it. That she was going to see him that night. That she would love him to take it off her... Rattle of key in belt...

Vibrations... Hormones shooting through her body...

I look from diary to door. It seems strange not to see the key poking out from the lock into the room. The door is open as usual: unlocked. The door is always open except when I go to Scotland for a month or Joanna's for the weekend.

Where have I got to?

Louisa is lying on the bed with her chastity belt newly removed; she is tense. I put my hand between her legs and caress her thighs, asking how she's been; she slowly relaxes. I hold open the lips of her sex and gently kiss and tongue her clitoris and the entrance to her vagina; she moistens and moans. I go on doing it, taking pleasure from her mounting pleasure...

I get up from the table and open my dictionary at the word cunnilingus. Cucking-stool, cucumber, cummerbund, curmudgeon but no cunnilingus. No cunt either. The book is hopelessly out of date and taboo-ridden and I must replace it.

Why did I perform oral sex on Joanna so rarely and so halfheartedly? The long and the short of it is that I have been too interested in my own penis for too long. Too focused on the pleasure I was getting from my dick. Need things carry on that way? I think a change has already taken place.

Wednesday, 22 November

Woke to re-read the new diary, key in slot at the top of every page. This is what needs to be said now:

The camera looks across at a long mirror standing in the corner of a bathroom. Her bathroom. Joanna enters the room in bra and panties and stands in the right foreground of the frame with her back to the lens. Her front is visible in the mirror. She doesn't look very happy. Her front is visible to herself as well. She stands there, arms by her side, staring into her none-too-happy face.

What is the matter? It's like this. She isn't getting the attention she needs from her partner. From me. She says I hardly ever compliment her on her appearance. That I don't pay enough attention to her body as a whole – looking, touching, kissing – never mind her genitals. She has lost confidence in her looks, her femininity. And when I occasionally criticize her appearance, the criticism cuts like a knife.

What is the matter? It's like this. She isn't getting the intimacy she needs from her partner. From me. We sleep miles apart during the week, which is all right by her. But when we settle down to go to sleep together at the weekend, I turn and face away from her. Which is not all right. For a long time she told herself it was OK, it was just my way. But it's not OK; she needs more.

What else? It's simple. I never tell her I love her. How can she believe I love her if I never say the words? And if I don't love her, then who does? If the person who shares his life with her can't bring himself to say he loves her, then what is there to suggest that he or anyone else loves her?

She finds all this a strain but bearable, until we go on holiday. Being together for a couple of weeks brings to light the lack of closeness between us. We explore the environment together, we dine together, we sleep together, but there is no special togetherness. She feels isolated, alienated and, ultimately, desolate. She feels that desolation now. She sees it in her face...

After a while she takes some cream from a jar to her right and rubs it along the inside of the metal waistband throughout its circumference. Her face relaxes somewhat as she loses herself in ministering to the needs of her body.

She slips her panties down to her knees and applies cream to her bottom, kneading her buttocks, and then to the chains, her hands passing up and down each one more often than is necessary to ensure there is an effective barrier between the metal and herself. She takes a length of padded material, folds it over the belt so that it hangs between the belt and the bruise at the top of her hipbone, sprinkles talcum powder on to the pad and repeats these steps with a pad at her other hip. She removes wads of cotton wool from behind the frontpiece, wipes her crotch carefully, applies both cream and powder to it, flicks her hand several times against her knickers and inserts a fresh pad of cotton wool either side of her abused pubic area.

She pulls up her panties, inspects her appearance in the mirror (without looking at her face, she doesn't want to face herself so soon after the last time and with nothing changed), turns round, looks over first one shoulder then the other while adjusting the lie of her knickers, and then exits the room – chin up, eyes false-bright, nose cutting through the air.

Undated

Walk down the steps to Joanna's basement flat for the first time in ages. Fish her keys out of the watch pocket in my jeans, where they've been pressed tight against my hip these past two months. And wonder if the procedure for getting in has changed at all.

I use the long key (two teeth) in the security lock then the brass key in the Yale and push the front door open. I hear the warning noise from the alarm. I use the other long key (three teeth) in the lock of the inner door and push that open. The beeping noise from the alarm is as annoying as ever. I walk briskly to the cupboard, jab the square-ended key into the alarm box and pause for thought before turning it ninety degrees to the left not right. Silence. It's quite a business getting into Joanna's flat but I don't resent it, I see the point. I sit down to wait for her.

She arrives and we kiss in greeting. She looks well and I tell her so before putting on the kettle. Soon we sit down on the sofa with our drinks and I put my arm round her shoulders. She feels tense. I tell her that it is a great shame I haven't been in the habit of telling her I love her because I *have* been loving her, albeit in a timid, non-demonstrative, anally retentive way. There is room for improvement; I intend to improve. But for starters I tell Joanna, quietly, that I love her, and kiss her cheek. She turns to look at me. I hold her gaze and say again, solemnly, 'I love you'. She smiles tentatively, still tense, but who can blame her for that? Not me.

'Now, about these Mediterranean holidays of ours...' I begin, with an air of embarrassment. I go on to say I'm sorry she's found them such a strain, but for me they have been too, though in a different way. Strange landscape, language, weather, culture make it feel like I'm living on another planet, which exhausts me. Clearly I don't have energy left over for her, for us. And the same thing is likely to happen the next time (where are we going – Mars, Pluto, Neptune...). So I suggest that as well as going away we spend a week or two together at home. Joanna guardedly welcomes this idea, which we discuss for a bit.

Joanna starts to relax. Frown lines disappear, the tension leaves her neck and she leans her head on my shoulder. I kiss her hair as I raise another bone of contention. My sleeping position. I tell her I'm going to scrap that old habit of turning my back to her. 'As simple as that?' she asks. I shrug and say that I really want to sleep face to face with my lover tonight, so, yes, as simple as that.

Joanna is obviously pleased by this last news. So I point out that there remains just one obstacle to us sleeping together in harmony that night. 'Oh, this old chestnut,' says Joanna, knocking her knuckles – muffled clunk – against her fanny. Perhaps its time has come, she admits. She'd love me to take it off her.

Joanna strips down to her chastity belt while I get out the key. I ask her to adopt the position, only to discover that the key will not turn the lock. Perhaps the mechanism has rusted or, more likely, got bunged up with creams and powders. I am sheepish about this. Sure, it was Joanna who chose to wear the belt, but it was me who... Certainly, it was she who applied the lotions and dusts, but it was me who... I take my share of the blame.

Joanna looks round and tells me I am using the wrong key. She is not at all impressed that I have mistaken the key to my room for the key to her chastity belt. According to her, it shows that my room is where I'd still like to be. I explain how the keys

33

have become mixed up via my diary; I explain that my own life and my life with her are both important to me and that occasionally they are bound to become entwined. Both explanations go down like lead balloons.

I extract a screwdriver from Joanna's toolbox. You see, it is not obvious, but there is a large screwhead at the end of the belt's frontpiece – close to where the chains start. And my guess is that if I undo it the whole bag of tricks will fall apart. I ask Joanna to sit on the floor, open her legs and lean back – supporting her weight on her elbows. She indignantly refuses: there is no way she is going to let me attack her nether regions with a screwdriver.

I tell her that she mustn't look upon it as phallic screwdriver versus female flesh but as metal against metal. All I want to do is use the only means at our disposal to ensure that we have an intimate time together. Can she not see that? Of course, if she wants to stay in the chastity belt for another day that's fine, I can collect the key from my room tomorrow, write up my diary, and we'll only have lost an evening, a night and the best part of a day together...

'Give *me* the screwdriver,' says Joanna.

I hand her the tool and she has a go. Not surprisingly, she can't get enough purchase. After all, her arms and the screwdriver are going in nearly opposite directions. Before giving me back the implement, she asks me to fetch a couple of towels from the bathroom.

I place the towels in and around the chastity belt in such a way that even should the screwdriver slip, it won't jab her thigh or her belly or her bum. But the tool is not going to slip, I assure her, as I fit the end into the slot of the screw. I give a tentative push and turn, but no dice. I set to with a vengeance. I am pushing hard and I am turning at the same time... I feel the strain going all through my body, right down to my toes. Come on! My heart is pumping blood into my face and suddenly I feel sweat bead my forehead. I relax. 'I'll have another go in a minute,' I tell her, knackered.

Joanna reminds me that the last time we were together in this flat we did a photo session at her instigation. By remote control she took a film of pictures of me with my hands round her neck. She lying on the floor close to where she lies now; me crouching over her torso with my hands clasping her throat. She tells me that the photos are in her bag if I want to have a look at them.

There are half a dozen 10 x 12 photos, which I spread out over the floor. Joanna has cropped the negatives so that the content of the images is ambiguous. It almost looks as if a man's hands are wrapped round his gigantic prick... Oh, I get it! The obsession with my own penis has been choking the life out of my partner...

I have another go. But it's no good, that screw is simply not meant to budge. Joanna points out that so far we have only tried it my way – brute force and bloody ignorance – which is not the only option. She suggests that a little lubrication might be in order. So I take the can of 3-in-1 from her well-stocked toolbox and I apply a few drops round the circumference of the screwhead. The oil needs to penetrate the chastity belt, to flow down along the length of the screw, and I am not sure this is happening. So I help Joanna to raise her legs into the air by grabbing hold of her ankles. I ask her if she can maintain that position for a few minutes with her hands supporting her raised hips. She assures me she can and she pulls a cushion under her back for additional support.

I have another go and the screw turns without difficulty. Oh, that feels good. I screw and screw again and now the bolt is loose enough to undo by hand. As the bolt is removed from the frontpiece the chains fall away from Joanna's loins.

'You little beauty!' I say. I don't mean Joanna, I mean the bolt.

'You little beauty!' says Joanna. She doesn't mean the bolt, she means me.

It seems I have been somewhat heavy-handed with the oil. Joanna's cunt is sopping wet. I think the best thing is if I suck the nectar right out of there. I think the best thing is if I lick her dry.

Saturday, 2 December

Dispensed with second diary. It took me too long to finalize the last entry in it – the book became a mess of deletion. Anyway, the key in the hole idea was naff.

I'll type the whole thing (which was always my intention), and that will put the material in a form I can send to Joanna. I might send a copy to Louisa MacIver, certainly I owe her something, but I'll have to take advice on that. Joanna's for a start.

What's the date? Saturday, 2 December. I have a week to let this stuff settle and to look forward properly to being with Joanna. That should be fine.

JOHN BYRNE   6 Dec '95

Dear Duncan McLaren,
Thank you on Tilda's behalf, for your letter re 'The Maybe', and particularly regarding the guy who made the comments –
I'm afraid Tilda has n't been well for some time but I know that she will drop you a line herself when she is better. Best wishes
pp Tilda Swinton   John Byrne

MAYBE NOT (2)

John Byrne: Scottish artist and playwright. *Tutti-Frutti* was a very successful TV comedy-drama series a few years ago; an exhibition of paintings, including a recently completed portrait of the Beatles, was showing in Glasgow last month.

John Byrne: his name featured in *The Maybe*. One of the glass cases contained correspondence between him and René Magritte, who empathized with the predicament of aspiring to be an artist while being stuck in a menial job. And I think an adjoining case contained the postcard reproductions of Magritte's work that the Belgian had sent to Scotland with his kind and encouraging letter.

And John Byrne was there in person at the Serpentine when I visited *The Maybe*. Leaning against a wall in the corner of the east gallery, where his Magritte correspondence was sited; with a view through two doorways to the north gallery, where Tilda Swinton was lying. While I was there he was talking to a fellow Scottish artist so he wouldn't have noticed the 'God, she's ugly!' incident. But even if he had been alert he wouldn't have heard the comment from so far afield. The security guard stationed a couple of yards from the head of the glass case would have heard all right, but couldn't have been expected to intervene in the circumstances.

The next day another incident took place. The same strange guy entered the Serpentine smoking a fat cigar. John Byrne was showing his compatriot a Magritte postcard. '*Ceci n'est pas une pipe,*' said John aloud and to his friend's amusement as the other strutted past them. Other entered the north gallery, approached Tilda's vitrine and stood staring at her sleeping (or not sleeping) face. He gibed, 'I've seen some ugly women in my time, but this bitch (OUI, CECI EST UNE CHIENNE), she takes the biscuit.' The security guard didn't even blink.

The last day of the show a final incident occurred. The strange bloke came into the gallery and nearly collided with John Byrne, who was standing between the rug from Freud's analyst's couch and the Magritte postcards. The guy heard John discuss Freud's theory of dreams in relation to Magritte's Surrealism. The guy stayed to listen to John discuss a particular Magritte painting – *Les Amants* – in connection with a hypothetical portrait of the Beatles. The Fab Four are standing in pairs, kissing, each with his head wrapped in a bedsheet. But who is who? That is up to the viewer. Some might interpret the scene as George kissing John and Ringo kissing Paul; others as John kissing Paul and Paul kissing John; and a few as John kissing Yoko and Yoko kissing Yoko.

Other entered the north gallery, approached Tilda's vitrine (is she or isn't she?) and shouted, 'PUT A PAPER BAG OVER IT, FOR THE LOVE OF CHRIST! And give me one too, because I'm going to be sick... '

The security guard yawned.

'... Too late... QUICK!... '

The security guard yawned hugely. He wished he was in bed all right, but not in a glass case surrounded by nutters.

'... Too late again... COME ON! COME ON! COME ON!'

The security guard yawned desperately. He didn't know how Princess Ti could sleep through such a stench, such a hullabaloo, such...

'... Too late for the third time of asking. God, look at my shoes! Not a pretty sight but prettier, surely, than the dog's breakfast in the sewage tank.'

The security guard yawned comfortably. In the knowledge that nutters came and went just like everyone else and that, with any luck, this one would be no exception.

I can't send this to Tilda Swinton, not until she's better anyway. And I can't end it any other way than by saying that my initial reaction to John Byrne's thoughtful postcard was to hope that Tilda was not seriously ill, and that if she wasn't well already she would be soon.

Tranquillity, Tilda.

INCOMMUNICADO

With Joanna to Chelsea, where she has been doing an M.A. in sculpture since the end of September.

The main element of the piece she is working on at the moment is a black and white photograph of a bedsheet which has been enlarged so that the creases and folds of material are very grainy and more or less life-size. The photo (four feet by three feet) is mounted – horizontally – on a foot-high stainless-steel box which was made for Joanna to her specifications by a machine shop that normally provides kitchen fittings for kebab houses.

Looking down on it, I think of a bed primarily – though it is neither the size nor the shape of a single or a double – and also, I suppose, of a sarcophagus. There are three fluorescent light tubes in the body of the box apparently, so that now a switch has been thrown the photograph glows in the corner of Joanna's workplace this winter's afternoon.

A short and a long side of the light box are about a foot from the walls that make up the room's corner. On each wall Joanna has painted a rectangle of a subtly different shade of white from the surroundings. These patches aren't the same size as the 'bed' – they are bigger – but they clearly refer to its presence. And, perhaps, to the essence of two people who have been lying there.

I feel that the patches successfully activate the space. Joanna agrees but thinks that something is missing. According to her, the piece is far too serene; not nearly disturbing enough. Which is why we have carried two sheets of glass (of a comparable shape and size to the other elements) from her car into the work space.

We lift one pane and place it fairly flat against the wall, behind the 'head' end of the bed but away from the corner of the room, so that there is only an overlap between the painted patch on that wall and the pane of glass. Joanna's hand and arm have just enough room to stick a strip of plastic on to the inside of the glass about a yard above the floor. She asks me to step back and tell her if it's straight. It is. So she uses her fingernail to rub each letter on the strip, which when peeled off leaves behind a line of text: I CAN'T HEAR YOU.

We place the second pane of glass over the first one. Then we turn it on its side, so that it is in portrait format, lining up the right-hand edges of both sheets – the edges closest to the corner of the room. By letting the second pane rest against the wall at a more oblique angle, it fills with reflections of bedsheet, which is an effect that Joanna likes. The gloss-paint patches on the wall did catch reflections late in the day when light in the room faded, but this is much more the degree of interaction that Joanna wants. I observe that the glass panes at once echo the straight lines and ethereal quality of the paint patches and literally reflect the bed, so they certainly provide a link between the work's original elements. Meanwhile, Joanna has chosen where to put the second strip of plastic and I help her to line it up as before: ET IN ARCADIA EGO.

Glancing across to another corner of the room, I catch sight of another graduate's work-in-progress. Shadows of soft toys – teddy bears mostly – have been painted low down on the walls. And on each grey shadow a yellow stream of piss has been painted, starting at toy waist level and descending to a puddle on the floor. After having been concentrating on Joanna's shades of grey for a while this work might have come across as an invigorating contrast, but it strikes me as too brash. Joanna tells me a little about her fellow student, a Japanese girl whom she gets on well with and whom she admires.

Nevertheless I turn away from the piss shadows and back to the matter in hand. Joanna *has* made it more disturbing by introducing the glass dialogue, but partly I am disturbed because I don't know what '*Et in Arcadia ego*' means. 'And I too in Arcadia', Joanna translates for me. She adds that it is a tomb inscription often depicted in classical paintings.

I have a problem with this because most people don't know Latin these days. The names of pop songs and TV programmes, yes; tomb inscriptions in classical paintings, no. I suspect that most people who view the work will not translate the line accurately. They might well take it one word at a time and get 'And in Arcadia egocentric', or egotistical. Or egomaniac.

And this compounds my problem. Because I know where the photo was taken. In Joanna's and my hotel room in Andritsena, Arcadia, the summer before last.

I air my reservations. But Joanna is sticking by her classical reference, which she feels is suitable, not least because of the allusion to a fractured communication.

Joanna cleans up her work space; I stand in the middle of it, admiring her handiwork:

I CAN'T HEAR YOU

ET IN ARCADIA EGO

15 December 1995

Dubcan McLaren
51 Southerland Road
Forest Hill
London SE23-2PS

Dear Mr McLaren,

Thank you very much for the piece of writing you sent us, <u>Soap Circle</u>. It is very warmly written, and it is nice to know that the exhibitions we do here can touch people. Do you publish any of your writing? Perhaps you could do an art diary for some magazine (Martin maloney at Lost in Space might have some suggestions).

I have sent your text on to Richard Long, who will, I'm sure, be very interested to read it.

With best wishes,

Lorcan O'Neill.

F I V E *POUNDS*

To the ICA, where there is a Glass Shelf Show of artists' multiples and editions.

A leaflet lists the participants. Bob Smith and Co. are here in force: Bob, Jessica, friends, contemporaries from Goldsmiths' and the Ken Ardley Playboys. Bob is offering concrete aeroplanes at forty pounds a throw. I'd like to buy one, both to see how it soars aloft and because I know he had to fork out tenners to persuade other members of the Playboys to dress up as the Beatles *circa* 1969 (long hair, beards and at least one – Ringo's – handlebar moustache) for a recent gig at a private view. But I've only got five quid.

For my fiver I could buy Martin Creed's *Work no. 88 – a sheet of A4 paper crumpled into a ball.* Or for a penny less I could buy Milo Garcia's *Five Pounds* – a limited edition of twenty-five. Martin is a mate of Bob's, while Milo exhibited with him in New Contemporaries. Despite the chance that *Five Pounds* may not be what it promises (just an A4 sheet of paper crumpled into a ball, perhaps), I plump for that.

The assistant at the bookshop congratulates me on my bold

purchase and produces an A4 sheet of paper. My heart sinks – as if I haven't got enough such pages fit for nothing but to be crumpled into balls – but it's simply a control list of numbers from 1 to 25, with space for name of purchaser alongside each number. The assistant sorts through a sheaf of pristine fivers which have been stamped, the stamp infilled with artist's signature and edition number. That's OK then, I'm getting a real fiver plus. So I write my name by number 12.

Out comes my wallet, in which there are three (!) shop-soiled fivers. So why not convert two of them into artist's money? The assistant tells me I'll have to write another name on the list. But that's fine, for in an unparalleled act of generosity I decide to buy a fiver for Joanna. I write her name in the space by number 14, which means that apart from number 1, which has been reserved, all the numbers up to 14 are spoken for. Several are available from 15 to 25, however, and my eye lingers on 22 for some reason. Luckily no name springs to mind: the limits to my largesse have been reached.

When I get home I write up my 'unparalleled act of generosity', though I don't arrive at that phrase until I've been right round the houses:

> inexplicable error of taste
> unusual lapse in concentration
> unfortunate stroke of luck
> unprecedented fit of nerves
> unbecoming bout of gangrene
> unbelievable load of old bollocks

• •

As soon as I settle on the appropriate phrase, it happens again. A second unprecedented fit of generosity. Because I DECIDE TO RETURN MILO GARCIA'S FIVE POUNDS TO HIM. I am so struck by the depths of character in me that this resolution reveals that I lay my forehead on the table and sob for a while.

Later, I realize I'm ten pounds down on the day.

Later, I realize I'm only £9.98, down but in the same instant I resolve to forward my 2p change along with the fiver to Milo. (The coin that I sheepishly stuffed in my coat pocket rather than the one in my wallet which no doubt got there following an everyday, self-serving, unambiguously satisfying transaction.)

Later, I realize I haven't been entirely honest with myself in this account. Bob Smith's name came to mind when I was looking at the blank space alongside number 22 on the list. So poor old Bob has lost out. But it is a sense of my own poverty – material and otherwise – that floods through me as I rest my head on the table again... in the dark now... in silence...

The phone rings. That'll be Joanna. I'll try not to tell her all about her Christmas present. But I know I'll fail, because the story – the way I'll tell it anyway (one to Joanna, two to *Big Issue* holders and three to Concrete Relief) – shows me in such a downright...what is the right word? <u>ALTRUISTIC</u> light.

unseeable stroke of tippex
invisible ghost of one
unusual lapse in concentration
unfortunate enlargement of original
unmistakable stink of rat
undeniable cry of 'Fake!'

....

John Stathatos
UNTITLED

Duncan McLaren
51 Sunderland Road
Forest Hill
London SE23 2PS

Tel.   0181 291 6979

23 December, 1995

Dear John Stathatos,

I was very interested by Clifford Myerson's comments in UNTITLED 8 on the decline of the viewer and the rise of the participant. I wonder if you think that the enclosed texts could provide a useful adjunct to the more objective reviews that appear in your journal.

In recent months I've also written about the work of Bob and Roberta Smith, Carl von Weiler, Tilda Swinton, Louisa McIver and Karen F, and Jo Bennett. If you'd like to read any of this, please get in touch. I will be writing more - a lot more, I hope - next year.

There is no need to return SOAP CIRCLE or FIVE POUNDS.

Best wishes,

Duncan McLaren.

A sheet of A4 paper to be crumpled into a ball.

W1NG

To Glasgow's Centre for Contemporary Art, where there is an exhibition of work by Dalziel and Scullion. The two water installations are interesting but it is *Wing* I have come to see.

The room is dark. Three circular pools of light on the floor – projected from the ceiling – show chickens on straw. The pale yellow birds are not fully grown, but they've lost their down and are covered in short, coarse feathers. The chickens lose resolution as I stand close to them, so I step back a distance.

A metal heater is suspended from the ceiling over each light patch. Their wide-coned shades direct heat – the elements and grilles glow red – down to the floor. I know this because I'm standing under the fourth heater, in the quarter of the room that doesn't feature a pool of light.

The room's central pillar stops me from seeing much of the projection in the diagonally opposite corner, but I have a clear view of the chickens in other circles. Some are feeding on either side of the line of their food tray. Some are drinking from the circular rim of a bell-like object suspended above the straw. The rest don't appear to be doing much at all.

The other elements of the installation are sounds – bird cries and music. Speakers mounted high in all four corners of the room are the source of both. The music could be one of Eno's ambient records, certainly it is contemplative and calming. The cries are from wild birds, though I couldn't say which in particular. Sharp calls come from first one speaker then another. It is as if the wild birds are flying just above this 'barn'. As anonymous as the chickens inside.

I walk to the far corner of the room. In the projection here there is neither food nor water, so what are these birds doing? I focus on one which is crouching on the straw. But it is a nearby chicken which moves, so I switch my attention to that individual. It stops after a few steps. I keep looking at it, but as another chicken pushes its way between my chicken and its nearest neighbour I decide to see what it's up to. It takes another step and sits down... There is usually movement somewhere in the circle but none of it to any great effect. Minor territorial adjustments. Or the release of nervous tension. Or simply exercise. But I don't know.

I wander back to the diagonally opposite corner and sit down on one of two chairs that flank the walls. My eye passes from the overhead heater down on to the featureless dark floor. Why is there not a fourth projection? (A bird cries out – plaintively; but the ambient music soon reasserts itself.) I can feel that this omission is going to trouble me.

W I NG

Two days later I'm in a hide by the River Tay near Kinclaven. Wooden boards all around me prevent any movements or noises I make from getting out to disturb the wild birds in the vicinity. But I can see out through a narrow horizontal slot in the north wall.

There is a group of black-backed gulls and a single cormorant standing on the shingle spit that comes into the middle of the river from the left. I think the gulls are great black-backed rather than lesser. Certainly they are an imposing sight with their black wings folded to their white bodies and their pale yellow beaks made vivid by a single red spot.

One gull's beak is tearing flesh from carrion on the spit's shoreline – possibly a salmon. No other bird is taking an interest in the corpse, but they may have eaten their fill of it before I came along. A couple of gulls are washing in the river, splashing their wings in the almost freezing waters. A layer of fat inside their skins or a coating of oil outside must retain body heat for them. A number of the other...

A swan flies over the hut and across the river. I see the big white bird and I listen to its wings slice rhythmically through the air: whoosh, whoosh, whoosh...

A number of the other gulls have already washed and are standing on the spit drying off. The cormorant is doing the same thing – albeit much more spectacularly – standing tall with its wings outstretched from its body, getting the most from the light north wind into which it faces. I can't tell if the cormorant and the gulls are gaining anything from their close proximity to each other, but neither is there sign of enmity between them.

I hear a goose overhead. A V-shaped formation comes to mind, but when the goose comes into view, flying downstream, it is alone. It calls again, raucously, with what seems like longing. A V-shaped formation in its mind too, perhaps. Or maybe the goose that floated by earlier was its mate. I don't know.

A piping call. I raise my binoculars to look at the spit again. A redshank has landed: long red legs and a long red beak, but it is a small, slight bird compared to the great gulls close to it. The wader probes away at the shingle right at the spit's end. I move my hands slightly so that the apex of the spit is in the middle of the binoculars' circular field of view. What do I see?

Redshank, dead centre. Four gulls on shingle – one eating, one preening and two facing downstream; cormorant facing cross-river, as majestic and as stationary as ever, though its wings must have dried long since. One gull in the water, washing its neck; a pair of black and white ducks with bold white blobs behind their bills on otherwise dark heads – goldeneye – conveniently swimming into the circle from bottom left. A lot of wild birds in a small space, coincidentally, beautifully, and surely not for long... The goldeneye swim through the circle and the redshank flies away. It is time for me to go too. First I write an entry in the visitors' book. I describe the weather conditions (clear) and the state of the river (high) and mention the birds I've seen. But I don't detail what I saw in the 'fourth projection'. And I don't add that a Tesco's roast chicken has been at my right elbow throughout, partly because I haven't paid it the slightest attention since putting it there.

I place binoculars and visitors' book in my bag (I want to take photocopies of entries made in it over the years) and I leave a note on the wooden bench, though I don't expect anyone will be along to read it: 'Visitors' book will be returned later today at which time the chicken will be disposed of one way or another.'

WING

It takes a crap afternoon to make me realize I had a really fine morning.

The scene from the hide is the same, but different. The sky has closed in, it's raining heavily and all the birds have gone off to find shelter. Leaving me with only the chicken for company.

I pull the bird towards me and bite from the untouched breast. I've been gnawing away desultorily at the other breast – the main bone is exposed – but now it's hard to get teeth to flesh without my cheeks, chin and nose rubbing against the greasy skin of the thing. I am not enjoying this meal.

I deliberately didn't eat at lunchtime so that when I got back here in the afternoon I'd be hungry. Would my interest in the wild birds distract me from my appetite? What wild birds? But in any case my plan was upset half an hour before I re-entered the hide.

Driving along. Five pheasants in the middle of the road ahead. I watched them get out of the way, except that one didn't. The cock was calling 'korrk-kok', and running in front of the car. I didn't take my foot off the accelerator. 'Clunk.'

I pulled up, saw the bundle lying on the road behind me and got out of the car, feeling every inch the hunter and gatherer. As I trotted up to it I could see that its neck was extended and its head was lying on its side, eye open.

Was it alive, then? My feelings of triumph disappeared and were replaced by uneasy ones. I stood over the bird and saw a single drop of blood seep from its half-open beak. Oh, fuck. I knew I ought to wring its neck but how did you do that? Well, the first step was to lay my hands on its throat, so slowly I bent down and reached my right hand towards the pheasant... which without any warning was up and running.

What a relief! I wouldn't have to wring anything's neck. On the other hand, my meal for two had got away. Or had it? It had stopped at the fence bordering the road from an oak wood. Had the pheasant shot its bolt? I walked towards it...and it ran fifty yards or so into the orange, bracken undergrowth. So that was that.

I got back into the car. Clearly its neck and legs were not broken. But what about its wings? And what about internal injuries? I didn't suppose that the bird would live to see another spring. I didn't suppose it would wake tomorrow morning.

The rain falls from top to bottom. The river rushes the water from left to right and out of view. I'd always slowed down for wildlife on the road in the past and will again in the future. But for now I'm left feeling sorry for the creature and guilty over my actions.

I take another bite out of the chicken, from its wing this time. As I chew the flesh I see the bead of blood emerging from the pheasant's beak in my mind's eye. And I feel sick to my stomach.

I can't eat any more chicken. I carry the corpse out of the hide and throw it on to the sandy shore. For the gulls or whatever.

Two days later I'm eating meat again. As usual. No, not quite as usual. Not chicken. And I spend a lot of time between meals looking at the re-sealable sticky label on the packet of pork sausages:

All livestock is reared on specially selected farms, chosen for the more traditional standards of farming practice they employ.

All livestock is allowed to roam Oak Wood in May when the bluebells are on display, and again in September when the leaves are on the turn.

Pigs may wander lonely as a cloud.

•

All livestock is reared on specially selected farms, chosen for the more traditional standards of farming practice they employ.

All livestock is reared on a 'live and let live' basis.

The animals are not killed and butchered as soon as they are mature.

The animals are never killed or butchered, although one was knocked down and run over by a moron recently.

They are automatically covered by Accident Insurance and are free to take out Personal Pension schemes.

Pigs may sleep easy.

•

Animals are reared outdoors or in large straw-bedded barns with fresh air and natural daylight.

Animals are taught the three Rs: Runtin', Rootin', an' Rollin'.

Animals are taught 'to do unto others as you would be done by'.

Animals are taught 'HOW TO SUCCEED IN BUSINESS'.

Pigs may piss about between lessons.

•

They are fed on a carefully selected cereal-based diet.

At Christmas their trough is filled with Brussels sprouts, peeled chestnuts and cranberry sauce; with mince pies for afters.

Given half a chance they eat crisps and drink lager.

Given the slightest opportunity they eat crisps and drink lager.

Pigs may drink lager.

•

They are fed on a carefully selected diet of current affairs programmes.

At Christmas their screen is filled with old films, the Queen's Speech and *Morecambe and Wise*; with *Carry on up the Khyber* for afters.

Given half a chance they watch *Coronation Street*.

Given the slightest opportunity they watch porn on satellite TV.

Pigs may watch Curly and Raquel.

•

They are free to move around.

They eat and shit and play and fight and feel pride sometimes (I dare say) and shame occasionally (don't we all) as they get on with living their one and only lives as best they can.

Drugs are never used other than for medicinal reasons and then under strict supervision of the vet.

Drugs are never used other than for recreational reasons and then under strict supervision of the author.

Pigs may fly.

SHIT SCULPTURE

To the London Contemporary Art Fair, but only because Joanna's told me that Bob and Roberta Smith are taking part.

It doesn't take long to pass through two floors of white cubicles showing – on the whole – uninspiring work at highly creative prices. I stop only when I come to Bob and Roberta's stand: concrete modules, an obscure video and a table supporting sculptures made from bits of paper and plastic and wood which are called – collectively and by individual name tag – 'Shit Sculptures'. The pieces are offered free of charge; several people are looking at them dubiously, fingering them furtively.

Patrick (a.k.a. Bob and Roberta) sees me and takes a break from work – the table is full in any case. Sculpting in public has not been easy, I'm told. Someone mistook his hat, which was kept under the table, for a free sculpture and walked off with it. And after several confrontations with spectators he's no longer working at the table but in the floor space behind it. Well-to-do women of a certain age have been giving him most hassle. They feel that his work lets down the tone of the whole exhibition. 'What *do* you think you're doing?' was how a particularly nasty and upsetting argument had started.

I mention the sculpture that Joanna was pleased to take away yesterday, and that I intend to write about it. I tell him also that I'm well aware that I've sent him several pieces of writing since last May. He only has to say the word and I'll stop pestering him with texts. But Patrick says that he enjoys receiving them. So that would appear to be all right.

I ask how things are going artwise. He didn't sell any concrete aeroplanes at the 'Glass Shelf Show' but hopes to have more luck with the concrete boats he intends to pull across a pond in Hyde Park; the Ken Ardley Playboys have a new single out and are playing in Manchester at the end of the 'British Art Show'; Jessica received an intriguing reply to her Hugh Grant letter, though it came too late for inclusion in the 'Cocaine Orgasm' exhibition...

And we chat about the art scene in general for a while before reverting to the work on the table in front of us. Which piece will I take? Patrick points out his favourite – a three-foot-long plank of two-by-one which has been crudely drawn on with a black felt-tip pen. However, I would feel uneasy walking about the Business Design Centre with this stick. Not because I think it's ridiculous, but because I think that most people here would think it looked – that I looked, with it in my hand – ridiculous. Anyway it hasn't got a label on it and I want one with the label.

I pick up a sculpture. Its most substantial component is the plastic lid of a cup whose circular grooves are stained with coffee. It also includes a sandwich-shop paper bag which has been scrawled on with a red crayon, and a plastic spoon-substitute. The 'spoon', the bag, the lid and that all-important label are joined together by bits of black sticky tape. 'What do you think of my choice?' I ask its maker. He looks at it assessingly. 'I think it's beautiful.'

Conscious of the little beauty in my left hand, I walk around some of the exhibitors' spaces down on the second floor. My impression is as before but I am brought up short by the sight of the Real Art Society PLC's showing. Three white walls hung with self-consciously tasteful paintings, plus smooth sculptures on plinths. This is fronted by a man sitting at a wide, wooden table reading a broadsheet newspaper.

I look around him and make a quick list of qualities the work lacks: imagination; vision; sense of humour or proportion; relevance to life at the end of the twentieth century – 'It's life, Jim, but not as we know it'; balls, balls and balls again – no balls... But I am getting carried away. Let's calm down a bit.

What about the bloke sitting there? Not an artist, of course, but the artist's representative. His classic tailoring is finished off with a bow tie and a pocket handkerchief. The handkerchief is scarlet but the tie isn't and my eye keeps switching back and forth between them in a futile effort to find an aesthetic connection between the two. This would be admirable if the mismatch was deliberate, but the dullness and respectability of the rest of his appearance suggest it's not... Why am I being so judgemental?

His solid, hardwood table is mainly highly polished space. But there are a telephone to one side, a fountain pen and a calculator to the other, and a neat pile of catalogues in front of him – not right in front, that's where his paper lies, but pushed towards the far side of the table. My side. I would like to march up to him and ask, 'What the fuck do you think you're doing?' But I haven't got the insensitivity...or the guts.

Very conscious of the sculpture in my hot left hand now – I am holding it label up, my fingers underneath the paper bag, my thumb pressing down on the plastic lid – I am itching to move on. A woman who has been scrutinizing a finely crafted object with the aid of a price list asks the dealer a question about the artist's credentials. As he goes to her side, I walk forward and deposit my shit sculpture – label still uppermost – on the handsome table.

I walk round the periphery of the exhibition telling myself to slow down... slow down. A sign saying 'Serious Art' makes me speed up again but I succeed in slowing to a saunter... and am feeling really quite serene as I complete my circuit of the building.

Dealer and client are standing with a catalogue now, talking business. My sculpture is no longer on the table, it is the only item in a splendid basket of woven wood underneath the table. Both heads turn as I bend down to retrieve my belonging. I straighten up under their close scrutiny. For some reason I am completely relaxed as I tell them, 'I went to a show by Bob and Roberta Smith and all I got was this *objet d'art.*'

•

I'm sitting at my table with a shit sculpture in front of me. Not my shit sculpture but Joanna's. I'm hoping it will prove to be as rewarding as my own.

A label is stuck on to a Pret A Manger bag, which is wrapped round a St Michael chocolate cheesecake tub. The 'back' of the sculpture is simply what's printed on the outside of the bag – an advert for a new product, LARGE CAPPUCCINO. Then there is a message printed in smaller font: 'If you would like to speak to me or one of my colleagues regarding anything to do with Pret A Manger, please feel free to call on 0171 827 6300. Thank you. Julian Metcalfe.'

I turn the sculpture round. I can smell ash in the tub and I can hear crumbs and see sugar sachets in the bag, but I'll find out more about these inner sanctums later. (That's the beauty of a shit sculpture – you don't have to be content with admiring its surface from afar, you can get stuck in there.) Now, in fact. I detach the label by releasing the two black sticky bits that join it to the Pret A Manger bag. The back of the label is blank except for a stamp which reads ANTHONY WILKINSON FINE ART SHOW FEB 96 T.0171 831 4269. So it's the other number if I want to talk about the large cappuccino, this number if I wish to discuss Bob and Roberta's show next month. I must try not to get the two confused.

The bag in turn is stuck in two places to the lid of the St Michael tub. I detach the tapes and release the neat, smooth-sided, transparent plastic bowl-on-a-base. The label on the lid shows a lot of info: product description, display and use-by dates, price, weight, ingredients, bar code and nutritional data; but I don't need to know any of it. I open up... Christ, what a stink. Under some cellophane there are half a dozen filter stubs and three roll-your-own dog ends. What little chocolate cheesecake that remains on the sides has been lightly dusted by grey ash, which lies in a layer on the bottom of the container. I close the lid and open the window of my room for a while.

I flatten the bag and note that it doubles as a post bag, with an 'affix stamp here' square in the top-right corner and instructions on how to seal the left edge before posting it off. 'Win a Caribbean Holiday for Two' it says. 'Simply tick one box below and send this empty bag to us.' And there is a customer-service quiz to the left and the Pret A Manger address in bold to the right.

The address has a tear across it. I put my hand into the bag via the rip and pull out the stuff which is pressed in the corner there. Three unopened sachets of brown sugar and a hairgrip. I have never really looked at a hairgrip before. It is a single piece of wire which is plastic not metal. The wire is doubled back on itself with three kinks in one half (to grip the hair, I suppose) and with both ends blunt (to avoid pricking the scalp, presumably). I lay it aside.

There is something else in there. A glossy, blood-red little delicacy. Gingerly I place it on the label. It is a woman's false fingernail, painted scarlet on the outside (to attract men, let's say), pale on the inside, with granules – dried glue, it must be – over the bottom half. I double-check that there's nothing else in the bag other than a few crumbs... but that's it.

I stand up from my chair, the elements of the sculpture spread out over the table. Only having stripped the piece down can I see what it might be about. Consumption (of cigarettes but not sugar; of sugar dressed up but not sugar *per se*); communication (through text on bag and tub and label; through hairgrip and fingernail); layers of consumption, each involving the question, How was it for *you*? I haven't made all the connections yet (I'll never make all the connections), but more might come to me.

A bag, a tub, a label, sachets, grip and nail. I could put them back together again but it wouldn't be quite the same, and, besides, I don't feel like doing that. What I feel like doing is dismounting from this armchair and winning the Caribbean holiday for Joanna and myself.

So I have to fill in the bag questionnaire. 'Which Pret have you just visited?' Bob and Roberta's Pret. 'Were we polite, helpful and fast?' Bob was polite, helpful and fast enough without ever seeming rushed... Now I have to tick one of the following boxes: 4-star (BRILLIANT), 3-star (GOOD, WELL DONE), 2-star (NEARLY THERE) or 1-star (KEEP TRYING). The options read more like a sentence, which I punctuate with exclamation marks not ticks: BRILLIANT! GOOD, WELL DONE! NEARLY THERE! KEEP TRYING!

I'll post that later to secure the holiday. And I must remember to give the sculpture label back to Joanna, since I promised to do that. But for now I'm going to mess about with the remaining elements. I open the tub, throw the cellophane and the fag ends into the kitchen bin, make a mug of tea while I'm out there and return to my table with tub in one hand, mug in the other.

I empty a sachet of sugar into the tub and discard the wrapper. Delicate brown granules on grey ash. I empty the second and third sugars so that there is a pile of glittering crystals in the middle of the tub, limiting the grey to the margins. By inserting the fingernail between the ends of the hairgrip I have a paddle with which I can move around the tiny sugar granules. As I paddle I stare at the back of the fingernail – that luscious blood-red.

I stop paddling when my eyes begin to sting. The sugar doesn't look so good now that it's been mixed with ash. I pour tea from mug to tub and the scene changes instantly. A muddy brown mixture. I stir, hoping to dissolve both the varnish and the sugar. But no varnish and not much sugar dissolve and the muddiness of the liquid is unchanged. I stop because my eyes are stinging again and because I have an idea. I put the lid on the warm tub, bin the thing and start to write...

A woman with an empty Pret A Manger bag in her manicured hand is loose in the London Contemporary Art Fair.

I can say a few things about the bag. It's been used to carry her lunch, it's going to be used in a Bob and Roberta sculpture, and it's going to win a holiday in the Caribbean for Joanna and me. But I can't say anything about the woman. All I know is that she drops the bag into the bin and then notices Bob.

Bob is sitting at his table getting on with his work. She approaches and stands directly in front of him. She scrutinizes the jumble, reads the labels, pokes one sculpture and flicks over another. 'What *do* you think you're doing?' she asks. Bob tells her that he's... practising his profession... honing his skills... soaking up punishment... pursuing a vision... failing to succeed... wooing an audience... minding his hat... mixing with concrete... thinking about boats... sniffing the roses... smelling a cat... sniffing the roses... definitely not smoking... waiting for Jessica... humming the single...

She leans across the table, knocking several shit sculptures on to the floor, and grabs Bob by the jersey close to the throat. She starts to shake him back and forward as she asks again, 'WHAT... DO... YOU... THINK... YOU'RE... BLOODY... WELL... *DOING*?'

The woman is half-way through her sentence before Bob manages to place his hands on her wrists. And by the time she's finished it he's slackening her grip. Finally Bob manages to throw off her hands. She sorts her hair, turns on her heels and clicks off in a state of high dudgeon. Bob looks distinctly rattled.

A couple of blokes who have noticed the scene approach. One picks a sculpture off the floor and puts it back on the table with a weak smile. Then he picks it up again, smiles with a little more conviction and walks away. 'If you've taken that because you're feeling sorry for me then you can bring it back right now,' says Bob, who hasn't regained his composure.

Meanwhile the second bloke has bundled five of Bob's creations into a carrier bag and is walking off with them without a word or a gesture. 'HOY! RETURN FOUR OF THOSE FUCKING THINGS IF YOU WOULD BE SO KIND!' shouts Bob, who still hasn't quite regained his equanimity.

Soon Bob calms down. Soon he picks up the Pret A Manger bag from the bin and pulls out the scarlet fingernail from the neck of his pullover. And pretty soon he finishes another shit sculpture (so called).

I WENT TO A SHOW

BY

ROBERTA & BOB SMITH

AND ALL I GOT

WAS THIS CRAP

TEXT.

Wednesday, 7 February

Phoned John Stathatos. He can't publish the pieces I submitted but suggests that I might review the forthcoming Bob and Roberta Smith show. I tell him that I certainly intend to go – I've received a postcard from Patrick inviting me to its launch – and that if I write anything about the work I will send it to *Untitled*.

Bob & Roberta Smith
Flawed

12 February - 9 March 1996

Launch 11 Feb 11:30 am
Serpentine Lake
Northside car park
by Serpentine Bridge.

Anthony Wilkinson Fine Art
29 Great Ormond Street London WC1N 3HZ
Tel: 0171-831 4269 or 0973 336662
Fax: 0171-831 9014
By appointment

Flawed

The front rooms of Anthony Wilkinson's flat – white cubes both – are the setting for Bob and Roberta Smith's first one-person show. Forget Roberta.

Walls display texts. In one room two brightly painted canvases (coloured letters awkwardly spaced over white backdrop) narrate tales concerning politicians: Harold Wilson mistakes which member of the Kennedy family he is talking to; Nixon's father hangs himself after being accused (falsely, it turns out) of defrauding his employer. In an early version of the latter text it is Kurt Cobain's father that commits suicide for identical reasons, so I'm guarded about interpreting it, or its neighbour, politically, and encouraged to engage with their black humour.

Next door, the texts are hand-scrawled on to large sheets of brown paper attached to the wall by black sticky tape. They concern art-world figures only, with one exception. It reads, 'WHEN WARHOL WAS A TRANSLATOR IN MOSCOW HE ONCE TRANSLATED A SPEECH BY STALIN AS "SOME OF YOU THOUGHT WE WOULD NEVER MAKE IT! WELL YOU WERE RIGHT! BUT YOU CAN _FUCK OFF_ ANYWAY!"' The overlay of arch-American artist on Communist dictator, of very free speech on strict censorship, is vibrantly absurd. And the failure spoken of is richly ambiguous.

Another text reads, 'ART FORUM ONCE ASKED JOHN BALDESSARI HOW HE GOT FROM CALIFORNIA TO NEW YORK? "IN A PLANE," he replied.' Well, Baldessari was interviewed by *Art Monthly* last year, where he said that nowadays a person of reasonable intelligence could come up with similar ideas to someone else in another part of the world. He then said, 'One thing that used to bother me on forays into New York... ' which might begin to explain why he would react to a presumably well-intentioned (hypothetical?) interviewer in such a brutally literal way... But there are many ways to follow up these texts.

All five of those on display show an interest in famous people and in human weakness – particularly communication dysfunctions. And a theme of the fifth is the mockery of those who take their success, or themselves, too seriously. In it, Lawrence Weiner, Steven Willats, Art and Language and Joseph Kosuth accuse each other in turn, and endlessly, of 'ripping me off'.

Happily, Bob Smith doesn't exclude himself from ridicule, as readers of his diary in this journal can readily see. Also, in *Humiliate* (a video that's not in the present show), Bob recounts to camera a series of reverses he has suffered – some of them self-induced – at the hands of powers that be in the art world.

The floors of both rooms here are given over to a single work. Below the brown-paper text walls, a fleet of concrete boats extends over the parquet. Most are about the shape of, and a little bigger than, a clothes iron; some have a wooden mast and canvas sails, others boast one, two or three concrete funnels.

Next door a video shows the 'launch' of the boats on the Serpentine the day before this exhibition opened, the private view as it were. A group of people are standing around chatting while some of their number drag the boats by lengths of string to and fro along the shore of the lake. This Sunday scene (reminiscent of Seurat's compositions on the banks of the Seine, though the century, the season and the types of boat are all decidedly different) is cut with an unchanging shot of balloons, the artist gratingly singing to a raucous and repetitive backing: 'I WANNA BE CREATIVE; I WANNA HAVE A GOOD TIME,' with 'I WANNA EXPRESS MYSELF' for occasional relief.

When a fellow artist knocks on the door to complain about the noise, it becomes clear that the balloon footage is shot in Bob Smith's studio. 'This is a really bad time, for me, for you to be doing this,' she says, echoing the wall texts. However, the conversation immediately becomes conciliatory as they discuss venues and dates for their imminent shows. And in the end it's left that Bob can racket on for an hour or so, but not all night and at the expense of her sanity.

The video cuts back to the Serpentine, with the plaintive song superimposed on the scene. Gently mocking all: a man peers intensely at his totally submerged boat, having expected too much, perhaps, of the lump of concrete he has attached himself to; a woman pulls her boat over the concrete foreshore in elegant sweeps that would transcend the limitations of the materials to hand; Bob Smith himself walks along the water's edge, looking at the camera knowingly, with his boat bobbling behind him in the shallows...

In one of the vignettes in the video *Humiliate*, the artist recounts, 'Sarah Kent wrote in the review section of *Time Out*, "Bob Smith's feeble foray into the artist as icon is a visual *Titanic*."' Well, I didn't see the show in question (if it existed), or read the full review (if it exists), but I find nothing feeble about this show's foray into the artist – amongst others – as small concrete boat-holder.

That is what I'll send to John Stathatos at *Untitled*. Maybe he'll publish it as it stands, but I can't leave it at that.

Rewind. There I am at the Serpentine: holding on to a concrete boat by its string (I WANNA BE CREATIVE); dragging the vessel a few steps along the bank (I WANNA HAVE A GOOD TIME); gazing dolefully at my sunken craft (I WANNA EXPRESS MYSELF). Scene and song whine on.

Cut to Bob's studio. His fellow artist knocks on the door and says, 'This is a really bad time, for me, for you to be doing this.' She goes on to say that she's got Bob's card inviting her to the launch, though it may turn out to be too cold for her.

Cut back to the Serpentine and there I am again. I remember this bit in reality... A child approaches me, pulling his concrete boat. The taut string is only a few inches above the ground so it is no trouble for me to step over it and allow him to continue on his way towards the artist at his tripod.

But once the boy passes beyond he stops and speaks to me. I can't hear him, so I crouch down to listen. Something is wrong, he feels, about the relationship between himself, the boat and the water, and the best thing would be if I pulled his boat along for him.

He can walk and he can talk but he's not very old this child, say three. I tell him that we're going in opposite directions (he's going up-camera, I'm going down-wind). But he doesn't understand this, or can't be bothered with it. Anyway, he still maintains that it would be for the best if I pulled his boat along for him, following him. Conscious that I'm in shot, worried about looking doubly ludicrous when attached to two concrete boats, I say to him (oh, I can't remember the actual words I used to round off our little chat, but something along these lines), 'This is a really bad time, for me, for you to be doing this.'

Actually I will send that last page with the others to *Untitled*. But not this one.

I feel that Patrick's taking the piss. The sequence of me with the boat is much longer than any other. Leaving me to bear the brunt of the I WANNA BE CREATIVE, I WANNA EXPRESS MYSELF gibe.

Paranoia? True, Patrick didn't know whether or not I'd turn up in response to his invite. True, I arrived on the scene as he was filming. True, I played with the boat happily enough and perhaps for longer than other adults. True, he hasn't messed about with the chronology of my sequence, or repeated bits of it as he has done with the studio interruption from his fellow artist. All true.

But say he is mocking me. Is that fair?... I have been using him in my work, so it's only to be expected, or at least perfectly reasonable, that he should respond in kind. And is it any big deal if he has? I'd like to think I've enough self-belief to put up with criticism, mockery or rejection.

All true, but... Perhaps my boat is getting into cold deep waters. However, for the time being I sail on...

UNTITLED ONCE
ASKED BOB SMITH
HOW HE GOT FROM
LONDON TO NEW
YORK. "WITH SHEETS
OF BROWN WRAPPING
PAPER," HE REP-
LIED.

Thursday, 15 February

I had a terrible dream last night. Over the phone, Patrick tricked me into inserting a piece of string through the knob of my penis. In a toilet, pissing everywhere, I decided to cut...

...the string that was carving me up in a horrific way. Just in time I realized it wasn't the string I was about to snip but the vital tube that transferred sperm from testicles to penis. I didn't make the cut, confronted Patrick with his wrongdoing (he wasn't interested and he wasn't accepting any responsibility for my actions), and I woke up feeling...*really* threatened.

Monday, 19 February

Joanna has advised me to rewrite the dream. She thinks I should try to get more distance from the subject, and, in the process, play up the humour. She is right, of course.

I had a strange dream last week. Over the phone, Patrick tried to persuade me into threading in a convoluted way a length of string through my genitals. I pointed out to him that in order to achieve such a result I would first have to create holes in my foreskin and scrotum. With a hammer and nails, he suggested. Righty-oh, I said, and went to work.

In a crowded public toilet, pissing everywhere, I decided to cut...

...the string that was carving me up in an unflattering and grossly inconvenient way. Just before doing so, I realized it wasn't the string I was about to snip but the vital tube that had transferred spunk from balls to prick most days of my adult life. I stood there aghast: one wrong move and I'd never fuck or wank again.

Meanwhile another bloke had just entered the gents and was pissing every which way – on me certainly. I wiped down my face for the second time in five minutes. 'God, what will I do?' he asked. 'Don't look down,' I advised him. His dick looked like it had been through a shredding machine. Yes, that's it. Something top secret had occurred to him and he'd written the gist of it on his dick. But in the interests of national security he'd been strongly advised – by someone who shall remain nameless – to put said dick through the shredder. I asked, 'Do you know Bob Smith, by any chance?' And he burst into tears.

I didn't make the cut and I got out of there and I confronted Bob with his wrongdoing. He wasn't interested and he wasn't taking responsibility for other people's moronic – completely imbecilic – actions. Bob was cool. I woke up feeling... strange.

Tuesday, 27 February

John Stathatos phoned to tell me that my review of Bob and Roberta's show was fine, he'd be printing it, though he may have to trim it down just a little. By the time my mind emerged from a complicated, deep-rooted and irresistible procedure of self-congratulation, the call was over. Over also was my interest in Bob and Roberta Smith's work, at least for a while. There are lots of other things going on and I can't wait to sample them.

So, that dream again. I come across Patrick by a lake. 'Hello, Duncan,' he says. 'Grab a boat.' I look down at the nearest boat's tether, which is strung with pins and needles. Patrick suggests that I pick up the string and wind it – clockwise or withershins, it makes no odds to him – around my dick. 'But Patrick,' I say, smiling, 'Why on earth would I want to do a thing like that?' He starts to justify himself, and to demonstrate what I should do; but I move away, skipping like a lamb and, in mid-skip, hooting like a wise old owl.

BOB'S HAT
(NEARLY STOLEN
RECENTLY.)
OB'S BOAT
ADE OF CONCRETE
OB MIXED
HIMSELF)
DO NOT
CUT

Thursday, 29 February

Joanna has been encouraging me to send 'Shit Sculpture' to Julian Metcalfe at Pret A Manger. I've been reluctant to do this; he's not an artist or an editor so what would it achieve? 'You never know' was and is her answer. Well, today I decided I would send it and I've achieved something already:

Julian Metcalfe
PRET A MANGER
Old Mitre Court
43 Fleet Street
London EC4Y 1BT

Duncan McLaren
PRET A LIRE
51 Sunderland Road
Forest Hill
London SE23 2PS

WHAT I DO

WHY I DO IT

Dear Julian Metcalfe,

Welcome to PRET A LIRE... a radically fresh approach. In seven years
PRET's passion and determination have taken me from a single room in
South London, to that same single room in South London.

Thanks to the British Sandwich Association for voting me Sandwich
Writer of the Year 1990-1996.

I continually strive for excellence and am never afraid to try something
new. I never/always compromise.

I never/always try to improve on nature by adding sugar, colourings,
chemicals or preservatives.

I have insisted my new text is made from paper derived from the Tampalla
Foundation in Finland where they currently plant ten ~~thousand~~ trees for
every one they fell.

My first "Helping the Homeless" truck is not yet on the road. But soon
many if not all of London's hostels for the homeless will be receiving
my fresh texts free of charge.

If you would like to speak to me regarding anything to do with my
writing please feel free to call on 0181 291 6979.

Thank you,

Duncan McLaren, 29. 2. 96.

P.S. Did you realise I introduce new texts each month?...

What do you think I should be concentrating on to improve my
operation?...

FOR LOVE OF TODAY

Sunday, 3 March

I go to Saatchi's – at Joanna's insistence – to see 'Young Americans' on the last day of the show. Five artists, but it is Sean Landers's autobiographical work – by turns arrogant, self-deprecating and narcissistic – that I look at for most of the hour. In particular, pinned to the walls are four huge texts which are fascinating, though I only have time to briefly consider each.

But I return to *For Love of Nothing* before leaving. It is nine feet high and fourteen across; a white primed canvas covered by a text made up of black, hand-painted, capital letters. I intend to read it systematically, albeit not from the beginning, but that's not what happens. I read bits of a line, then skip up and across and read a bit more, and so on. Why? Although it is possible to stand in one spot and read a complete line from left to right, it is then difficult to locate the beginning of the next line. Take a line in the middle of the two hundred or so which ends 'my most secret and humiliating wish'. The eye flashes back through fourteen feet of canvas on the lookout for continuation of the sentence, inevitably wavers on the way and ends up jumping about in search of the correct re-entry word. Hard work. All the more so in the knowledge that Joanna is still waiting for me in the car... I have to go.

Monday, 4 March

Overnight I was thinking about the text. I reckon that if I mentally flagged the first word of a line, when I returned to the left edge of the canvas I'd simply locate the flagged word, transfer the flag to the word immediately underneath and carry on reading from there. I'm not sure how easy this would be in practice, but I'd love to give it a go.

I phone Saatchi's to ask if there's any chance I can come along to see the show again, but am informed that the work is already being packed into crates. I ask where Sean Landers will next be showing and am advised to contact his dealers – White Cube – where he had an exhibition a couple of years ago. (I missed that completely.) She goes on to tell me that the catalogue to 'Young Americans' reproduces the works. It retails at £19.95 but if I send a cheque for £14.95 to the gallery they'll post the book to me. Am I in a hurry for this? No – I'm in the middle of writing a piece on Joseph Beuys and Andy Warhol.

I zoom into town and inspect the catalogue in Dillon's. The whole of *For Love of Nothing* is reproduced on a single page but I can just about decipher the words. I reckon that a magnifying glass will make the text readable so I hand over the money – including the extra fiver – and make my way to Westminster Art Library on the off-chance of finding a review of the earlier show as well as the latest one. *Art Monthly*, July/August 1994, provides what I want, and informs me that the text was exhibited in White Cube opposite another called *Self-Something*, which I also saw yesterday.

Home again, I compare the *For Love of Nothing* illustration with the work of another White Cube artist – Hiroshi Sugimoto's *Seascapes*. There is a kind of horizon in the Landers text but the bottom half of the painting would have to be darker for the likeness to be marked. However, the comparison is not irrelevant because, when I turn back a page in the Saatchi catalogue, I see four seascapes by Sean Landers, one of which is a text otherwise in the style of *For Love of Nothing*. I dip into the seascape with the aid of a magnifying glass, but can only do this for so long at a time.

Tuesday, 5 March

I begin to transcribe *For Love of Nothing* from a photocopy (200 per cent enlargement on to A3 paper – no need for me to use the magnifying glass). By the time I've filled three pages with neat black capitals of my own I'm eighteen lines down the canvas, about 10 per cent of the total. I give my eyes and my wrist a rest and consider what I've written.

The artist starts by saying that the text is being made for a show in England. Sean is apologetic about his use of English and mentions that when an advertiser in the States wants an actor to appear intelligent they use someone with a British accent. Following this sycophancy, he coyly mentions the War of Independence... His first rant is about having grown up in the age of AIDS rather than the free love era of the sixties. He hates baby-boomers: 'fuckin loafer wearin, BMW driven, cappacino drinkin assholes'. He has to switch his studio lights on, explains that he's working on a scaffold, bemoans the lack of a single US president in his lifetime that he can be proud of, and sits down for a smoke... Next it is a new day. He's feeling uninspired and could do with a nude female model to get him going...

I return to my photocopy, but not to transcribing, which takes too long. As I read I use a highlighter and so I get to the end of Sean's second day. He goes on in a candid and confessional way about his objectification of women, then talks nostalgically about his grandfather. He worries about being stereotyped as a writer or an artist, before a pain in his kidney causes him to break off and to bemoan his lack of healthcare insurance. He asks, 'How does one produce great art with an average mind?'

then congratulates himself on keeping the lines of his painting relatively straight. He ends the radio-accompanied day by quoting Elton John: 'If I was a sculptor but (end of line) then again no.' Which works well on my large sheet of paper but which must work even better on giant canvas – the mind (average?) completing the sentence long before the eye returns to the left edge for confirmation/duplication.

I read more. What's eating him this day is that publishers have rejected his book. His first choice, Vintage, have joined ten other houses by suggesting that the work is not a commercial proposition. Sean reckons he'll keep on writing regardless, that he'll probably write well in his forties, and that for now he should concentrate on making art. He prays. He wonders if the God he is praying to exists only in his mind. Suddenly he is back on the subject of pornography, his appetite for visual stimulation, but this turns sentimental: 'After last summer I don't know if I'll ever love again.' Poor Sean... Back from lunch he admits that he fears the reader's judgement. All he wants is for people to like him and to admire his art... A new day – St Patrick's. Sean suspects that he was ridiculous yesterday and he doesn't write much. Even so I don't manage to read all of it. My eyes are tired. The writing is getting fainter. I'd better leave it at that.

Wednesday, 6 March

I've just read about Sean's next day – which would be Friday, March 18 1994 – directly from the catalogue illustration. I held magnifying glass in right hand and kept my left index finger at my place on the left margin. This technique isn't perfect: my eyes feel strained and moisture has passed from my finger and the side of my hand on to the paper, which has warped. But it's enabled me to make progress.

Sean feels good: it's a warm spring day and he's looking forward to spending the weekend in Massachusetts with his brother, who has a nine-day-old son; the *LA Times* printed a big profile article on him the day before; the lines on his painting

83

are still straight. But his mood changes. He feels he is droning on about nothing, that he hasn't accessed his inner poet and that reading his text is about as exciting as staring out of the window at an unchanging view...

He draws attention to a 'visual event' that's taken place in the work. The writing is smaller since he stopped using the scaffold. This wasn't deliberate, but now that he's noticed it he wants the shrinkage to be more pronounced. So he goes down two brush sizes. I check the effect of this on my A3 copy and, sure enough, the writing is now smaller and lighter. I can make out words here and there but not consistently. Back to the catalogue.

Sean is still having a bad day, stuck in the 'dulldrums'. Why can't he be happy? he asks himself. He has a beautiful girlfriend and a wonderful life. 'Average man from the middle of the middle class with nothing to hang his angst ridden hat on'. He thinks he has gained ten pounds. He is thirty-one years old. 'An aging loser.' 'Youth where have you gone?' But he looks in the mirror and discovers he isn't fat at all. End of day.

I've now got a bookmark serving the double purpose of keeping my eye on the correct line of text and stopping perspiration from my left hand further damaging the catalogue. Nevertheless I'm finding it hard going. The writing is uncomfortably small now – I miss the odd word even with the magnifying glass. And my left eye – I keep the right eye shut some of the time – is feeling the strain and needs to be rested every few minutes. Moreover the writing concerns less. It is more difficult to summarize what is being said, so I won't even try. I'll go back to transcription if only for a line or two. Line 107:

'SUCCESS. THAT THE WHOLE WORLD'S UNFAIR IF I CAN EXIST. YOU PROBABLY THINK I'M RIPPING SOMEONE OFF. WELL FUCK YOU TOO. I'M SICK AND TIRED OF COWERING IN FRONT OF AN UNSYMPATHETIC ART WORLD, COMPRISED MOSTLY OF PEOPLE FAR DUMBER THAN MYSELF WHO INEVITABLY ARE BITTER AND ENVIOUS. IT'S AS OLD AS ART ITSELF AND I DON'T CARE ABOUT IT ANYMORE. FUCK YOU IF YOU HATE ME. REALLY, I WELCOME YOU'RE HATRED. I HATE YOU TOO. I'M

TIRED OF SEEMING LIKE'

And here is line 130:

'SLEEVES. IF YOU'RE SO SMART WHAT ARE YOU DOING READING THESE WORDS OF AN IDIOT? SURE YOU FEEL SUPERIOR TO ME BUT WHY? WHAT DO YOU DO THAT'S SO FUCKING GREAT? I REALLY AM SICK OF COWTOWING TO IDIOTS...'

I need to rest my eye. What's more, my vision has gone blurred. Not my left eye, which has been doing the scrutinizing, but the right,which has been tightly shut. So it's probably just gummed up. But I'd better keep tabs on the situation. And I'd better keep clear of the magnifying glass. First let it remind me how the whole text ends: '... LET ME PUT IT THIS WAY. I AM HERE NOW, AND I WILL NOT ALWAYS BE.'

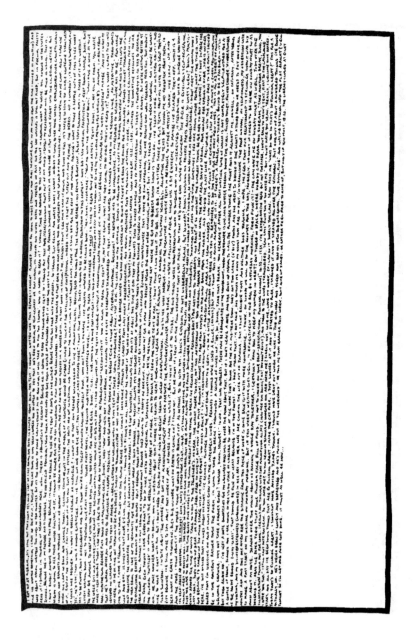

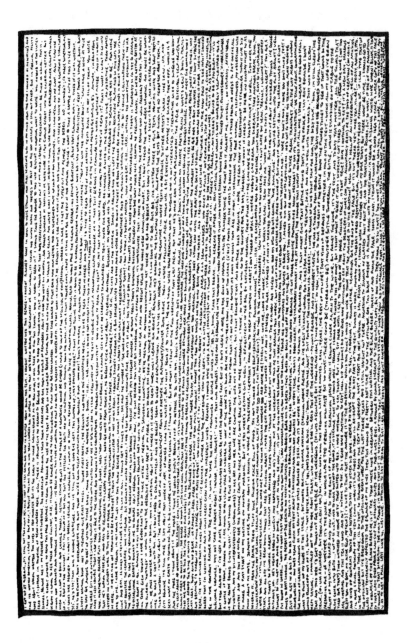

Friday, 8 March

Evening. Spoke to Joanna on the phone who sounded bullish about work. In return, I trumpeted elephantine. I'm much too close to what I've been doing this week and it will be fascinating (trunk tugging?) to find out what my lover thinks of this text. If she thinks it's self-serving, Landers-aping, egotistical wank – which it is – without any redeeming qualities – which it does have, surely – then maybe it won't see the light of day. I'll use the copier to reduce it further so that the whole text, pages i to ii, fits on to a single sheet of loo roll.

But that was a funny feeling I had this morning. A strong sense of being. And what Joanna or anyone else thinks won't change that.

I hope she likes it, though, and would like to see it blown up on to public walls. For the Love of Today. Today, yesterday, tomorrow... Good.

Thursday, 7 March   (And into Friday morning. Revisited.)

I GOT UP AT 9.45 A.M.. IT'S STILL NOT TEN O'CLOCK YET. ONCE I GET UP I GET GOING AND TOD
AY I'M EXCITED ABOUT DOING THIS TEXT. I HAVEN'T WRITTEN LIKE THIS BEFORE - I HAVEN'T P
LANNED WHAT I'M GOING TO WRITE (THOUGH THAT FIRST SENTENCE WAS IN MY MIND FROM T
HE TIME I LOOKED AT MY WATCH), AND
ONCE I'VE WRITTEN SOMETHING I CAN'T GO BACK ON IT. I SUPPOSE THIS LAST THING IS WHY
SEAN LANDERS HAS SO OFTEN TO SAY THAT HE'S BEEN BORING, OR SELF-CENTRED, OR JU
ST WRONG. IT'S CLOUDY AND WINDY TODAY AND THERE'S NO POST AND THE LOO UPSTA IRS
IS STILL NOT FIXED. BUT I'M FEELING PRETTY
GOOD ABOUT HAVING WRITTEN TEN LINES IN TEN MINUTES. BUT IT'S TOO EARLY TO MAKE C
ALCULATIONS AS TO HOW LONG IT WILL TAKE TO FILL THIS 'CANVAS'. WHO IS GOING TO REA
D IT? I SHOULD TAKE THE ANSWER TO THIS INTO ACCOUNT IN CHOOSING WHAT TO WRITE. WI
LL ANYONE IN THE STATES
READ IT? I SUPPOSE I'M THINKING OF SEAN LANDERS HERE. WELL, THERE IS ABSOLUTELY N
O REASON TO BELIEVE HE IS GOING TO READ THIS SECOND-HAND TEXT SO I SHOULD PUT TH
AT HOPE/FEAR/DELUSION RIGHT OUT OF MY MIND. I EXPECT MY READERSHIP WILL BE MUCH
AS USUAL. THAT IS
JOANNA, BECAUSE SHE IS MY PARTNER AND SUPPORTIVE. THE ODD FRIEND, PROVIDING I S
END THEM A FREE COPY AND GIVE THEM A COUPLE OF REMINDERS ABOUT IT OVER THE NEX
T SIX MONTHS. AND PERHAPS SOMEONE AT SAATCHI'S OR WHITE CUBE IF I PUT ENOUGH EFF
ORT INTO THE COVERING LETTER. BUT
I DON'T EXPECT ANYONE TO READ THIS PAGE BECAUSE I'M GOING TO REDUCE THE SIZE OF T
HE TEXT BY 200% ON THE COPIER BEFORE PUTTING THIS PAGE WITH THE OTHERS. SO I SHO
ULD JUST RELAX AND WRITE WHAT I WANT. NOBODY IS GOING TO SEE THESE WORDS EMBLA
ZONED OVER GALLERY WALLS.
NOBODY IS GOING TO SEE THESE WORDS FULL STOP. 10.25. IT SHOULD BE EASIER FOR ME
TO GET THIS WRITING TO FLOW THAN FOR SEAN LANDERS. HE MUST TAKE LONGER TO PAINT
EACH INCH HIGH LETTER AND HIS SENTENCES MUST GO COLD ON HIM SOMETIMES. ALSO I C
AN SPELL AND HE CAN'T. ALSO I CAN USE
COLONS AND BRACKETS AND HYPHENS WHICH HE DOESN'T. I'VE BEEN DOING THIS TYPE OF
WRITING FOR HALF AN HOUR AND ALREADY I'M A MASTER OF IT - IS THAT WHAT I'M SAYING? N
O. BESIDES I DON'T SEE MUCH SIGN OF COLONS AND SUCH IN THIS. IT'S SAFER TO STICK TO
SIMPLE SENTENCE STRUCTURES
WHEN YOU CAN'T GO BACK AND CHANGE THINGS. GETTING STUCK OR LOST IN THE MIDDLE O
F A SENTENCE WOULD BE EMBAR (I HAVE TO LOOK UP THE SPELLING OF THIS) RASSING. IND
EED I'M SURE I'D GET THE TIPPEX OUT AND REMOVE THE DEBRIS. NO I WOULDN'T; I'D MAKE S
OMETHING OUT
OF IT. RAIN ON THE SKYLIGHT. FIRST THE SOUND OF IT BUT NOW JUST THE PATTERN. THE DR
OPS ARE NOT COALESCING AND RUNNING DOWN THE GLASS, IT WAS A LIGHT SHOWER ONLY
. I HOPE IT STAYS DRY FOR THE REST OF THE MORNING BECAUSE I WANT TO TAKE A SAMPLE
COPY OF THIS TO SEE WHAT
IT LOOKS LIKE REDUCED. DO I WANT IT BARELY LEGIBLE OR ILLEGIBLE? I WANT IT SO THAT A
NY READER WOULD NEED TO USE A MAGNIFYING GLASS. HAVING READ THIS WHOLE PAGE T
HE GENTLE READER - HIS RETINA BURNT OUT, BLACK SPOTS PLAGUING HIM - IS ASKED IF IT
WAS WORTH IT.
"YES," HE'D SAY, "THAT WAS A UNIQUE EXPERIENCE. AND I'VE STILL GOT ONE GOOD EYE LEF
T. THIS GUMMED UP LAZY BASTARD HERE." I DON'T THINK TELLING JOKES IS GOING TO BE A
WORKING PROPOSITION IN THIS CONTEXT. WHY DID I SAY WORKING PROPOSITION? KEEP THI
NGS SIMPLE, DUNC. DON'T
TRY TO BE FUNNY, DON'T OVERELABORATE, AND DON'T THINK YOU'RE GOING TO GET AWAY
WITH CALLING YOURSELF DUNC. WHY NOT? DUNC'S MY NAME. I'VE ALWAYS WANTED TO BE
CALLED DUNC. "HEY, DUNC, OVER HERE." "HELP ME WITH THE HOMEWORK, DUNC." "CAN I H
AVE A LOOK AT YOUR
LATEST WRITING, DUNC. NOT TO MENTION YOUR FIRST NOVEL. YOUR FIRST NOVEL, THE SEC
OND AND THEN THE ILLUSTRATED NOVEL. I'D LIKE TO READ THEM IN ORDER AND <u>THEN</u> I'D LIK
E TO READ SOME OF YOUR ARTISTS' TEXTS, DUNC. OH, NOT ALL OF THEM. YOU WRITE
TOO FAST FOR ANYONE TO KEEP UP WITH YOU THESE DAYS...MUCH TOO FAST...FOR ANYON

E ELSE...DUNC." 11.01....11.48. WHAT DID I DO MY 8 THAT WAY FOR? I WAS TOLD IN NO UNCER
TAIN TERMS ON MY FIRST DAY AT SCHOOL NOT TO USE THE TWO CIRCLE METHOD FOR WRITI
NG 8S. ANYWAY, I'M BACK FROM

THE COPIER (IT'S COLD OUTSIDE; WINTER AGAIN) AND PLEASED WITH MY COPIES WHICH ARE
AT 50% NOT 200 AS I SAID A FEW LINES UP. THE TEXT IS LEGIBLE WITHOUT A MAGNIFYING GL
ASS, HOWEVER. OR IS THAT JUST BECAUSE I'M FAMILIAR WITH WHAT'S WRITTEN? MAYBE. AN
D IF I WANT TO

MAKE IT LESS LEGIBLE THEN I CAN TAKE IT BACK TO THE COPIER AND GO DOWN A FEW GEN
ERATIONS. NO PROBLEM THEN - GET ON WITH IT. WHO IS GOING TO READ THIS TEXT? NO, NOT
THAT AGAIN. WHAT ARE THEY GOING TO DO ONCE THEY'VE READ IT? THAT'S WHAT I WAN T TO
GO INTO

NOW. HYPOTHETICAL READER PUTS DOWN HIS MAGNIFYING GLASS, BLINKS, GOES "WOW" A
ND GETS OUT A PAINTBRUSH. ON A CANVAS 9FT BY 14FT HE CAREFULLY TRANSCRIBES MY
TEXT. WORD FOR WORD. HE CHANGES A WORD IN THE SECOND LINE, AN ADJECTIVE, THEN A
DMITS

THAT HE'S WRONG AFTER ALL AND HAS TO REINSTATE MY CRAPPY ADJECTIVE. WORD FOR
WORD FROM THEN ON, HE DOESN'T EVEN THINK ABOUT ALTERING ANYTHING. BOLLOCKS! HI
S RESPONSE HAS TO BE IMAGINATIVE. AS MY RESPONSE TO SEAN'S WORK HAS TO BE. FRO
M LARGE

LETTERS ON GALLERY WALL TO TINY TEXT ON PAPER TO LARGE LETTERS ON GALLERY WAL
L TO TINY TEXT ON PAPER. GOING SOMEWHERE? FUCK. STOP. 12.05... THE CATS ARE IN THE
KITCHEN. JAMES IS AROUND AND HE'S LEFT THE DIVIDING DOOR OPEN AGAIN AND SO THE C
ATS ARE

UP HERE. IS HE OR IS HE NOT TRAINING TO BE A BUS DRIVER? SURELY THE TRAINING COURS
E IS NOT IN HIS ROOM. I RECKON JAMES'S CAREER AS A BUS DRIVER LASTED TWO DAYS AND
HE NEVER GOT TO PUNCH A TICKET OR BEND THE RULES FOR AN OLD LADY. JAMES IS QUIET
THOUGH, SO IT'S ALL

ONE TO ME. I HAVE A FEELING I'M NOT GOING TO GET INTO THIS AGAIN BEFORE LUNCH. LUNC
H? SOYA MINCE, PARSNIPS AND CARROTS FROM LAST NIGHT NEEDS REHEATING. AND HAVIN
G MENTIONED FOOD MY MORNING'S WRITING IS OVER. I'LL DO A QUICK CALCULATION THEN I'L
L

COOK AND EAT. 22 LINES OF TEXT OVER 6.5 CMS. 24 CMS IN ALL. I SHOULD GET 81 LINES IN A
LL. SAY HALF THE NUMBER IN 'FOR LOVE OF NOTHING'. WILL I FINISH IT TODAY? I DON'T KNOW,
IT DOESN'T MATTER. COOK AND EAT. 12.22...13.03. WATCHED THE LUNCHTIME HEADLINES.
T HE IRA

WON'T REINSTATE THE CEASEFIRE. WOE IS IRELAND. BUT ENOUGH OF WORLD AFFAIRS. I HA
D A SHIT DOWNSTAIRS, WHICH WAS FINE. AND IT'S ABOUT THIS TIME OF DAY THAT MY THOUG
HTS TURN TO NAKED WOMEN AND MASTURBATION. BUT TODAY IS THURSDAY SO I'LL TRY TO
REFRAIN.

THE IDEA BEING TO SAVE UP MY SEXUALITY FOR THE WEEKEND WHEN I'M WITH JOANNA. THI
S DOESN'T ALWAYS PAY DIVIDENDS HOWEVER. IF JOANNA FEELS THERE'S EMOTIONAL DIST
ANCE BETWEEN US, THEN SHE WON'T MAKE LOVE. LEAVING ME FEELING RANDY. BUT WE'RE
GETTING BETTER AT

RE-ESTABLISHING RAPPORT QUICKLY SO I'VE NO QUALMS ABOUT KEEPING HANDS OFF MYS
ELF NOW. I'VE JUST RE-READ THIS LAST BIT, WONDERING IF IT WILL OFFEND JOANNA. IT'S UN
FORTUNATE THAT I HAVE TO RISK UPSETTING THE ONE PERSON WHO WILL PROBABLY REA
D THIS. THAT DOESN'T

SEEM RIGHT AT ALL. ACTUALLY I'M NOT SEEING HER TOMORROW NIGHT BECAUSE SHE'S GOI
NG TO A PARTY ON HER OWN. ON THE LOOK OUT FOR A MAN WHO DOESN'T SPEND THE WHO
LE WEEK WANKING, NO DOUBT. BUT I DON'T SPEND THE WHOLE WEEK WANKING AND I WON'T
BE WANK-

ING TODAY EVEN THOUGH I HAVE EVERY RIGHT TO DO SO SINCE WE'RE NOT MEETING TIL SAT
URDAY LUNCHTIME. WE'RE MEETING AT ANTHONY WILKINSON FINE ART WHERE THE BOB AN
D ROBERTA SMITH SHOW IS STILL ON. I'VE SEEN IT ONCE, AND WRITTEN ABOUT IT, AND

THE JOURNAL 'UNTITLED' IS GOING TO PRINT THE OBJECTIVE REVIEW PART OF MY PIECE. ON
LY JOANNA HAS SEEN THE WHOLE TEXT SO FAR. I DON'T THINK I CAN SEND IT TO BOB. POOR
BOB, I'VE WRITTEN THREE OR FOUR TEXTS ABOUT HIS WORK AND SENT THEM TO

HIM. HE MUST WONDER WHAT I'M DOING. WHY AM I WRITING ABOUT HIM? WHERE IS IT GOING TO
LEAD? WHEN WILL I LEAVE HIM ALONE? ACTUALLY, HE'S HANDLING THE SITUATION SENSIBL
Y. ACCEPTING THE TEXTS BUT GIVING ME NO FEEDBACK ABOUT THEM. I'D

LIKE TO HAVE A CHAT WITH HIM. BUT I DON'T NEED TO EXPLAIN MYSELF AND HE DOESN'T SE
EM TO NEED AN EXPLANATION. SO WE'LL SEE WHAT HAPPENS. AND IN THE MEANTIME I'LL W
RITE RESPONSES TO OTHER ARTISTS' WORK. LIKE SEAN. OH, AND
TILDA SWINTON. I WROTE ABOUT 'THE MAYBE' AND GOT AN ACKNOWLEDGEMENT FROM HER
PARTNER, THE PLAYWRIGHT/PAINTER JOHN BYRNE. THEN I WROTE A FOLLOW UP PIECE WHI
CH WAS A BIT EXTREME SO MAYBE I'VE SCARED THEM OFF. WHICH IS A
PITY BECAUSE I'VE STILL MORE TO SAY ABOUT THAT WORK OF ART. OF COURSE I CAN STILL
WRITE IT, BUT I WON'T SEND IT TO TILDA. THE ONE THING WORSE THAN PRESENTING WORK
TO SOMEONE WHO IS NOT INTERESTED, IS PRESENTING WORK TO SOMEONE WHO WON-
DERS WHAT ON EARTH IS GOING ON. DOES BOB WONDER WHAT ON EARTH IS GOING ON? I THI
NK NOT. BUT HE MIGHT IF I SENT HIM THE FULL VERSION OF THAT LAST PIECE. NOT THAT HE'
D HAVE GOOD CAUSE FOR CONCERN. THE PIECE IS ESPECIALLY SELF-REVEALING.
AND THE MORE I THINK ABOUT IT THE MORE I THINK HE WOULD SIMPLY SHRUG IT OFF AS NOT
HING TO DO WITH HIM. DUNC'S EXPOSING HIS SOFT UNDERBELLY AGAIN, BUT SO WHAT? DUN
C'S EXPOSING HIS PRIVATE PARTS AGAIN, SO WHAT'S NEW? DUNC'S PRACTIS-
ING SELF-ABUSE AD NAUSEAM... <u>NO I AM NOT</u>! GOOD, THAT'S SETTLED THEN. 13.47...14.40. I
T'S STILL COLD OUTSIDE AND THE COPIER IS STILL WORKING. THE CATS ARE DOWNSTAIRS.
THE GREY ONE IS CURLED UP ON A THICK RUG, AS WARM AND SECURE AS FELINELY POSSIB
LE. I DIDN'T MEET THE WOMAN W H O I
USUALLY MEET IN FOREST HILL. SHE WALKS SO SLOWLY, WITH SUCH LONG RESTS, THAT SH
E IS ALMOST ALWAYS TO BE FOUND SOMEWHERE BETWEEN HER HOUSE AND SAINSBURY'
S. SOMETIMES SHE ASKS ME THE TIME. SOMETIMES I SEE HER ASKING OTHER PEOPLE WHA
T THE TIME IS. WHY
DOES SHE HAVE TO BE TOLD THE TIME EVERY FIVE YARDS? IS SHE TIMING HERSELF? IS SHE
TRYING TO BREAK THE RECORD (HER OWN PERSONAL BEST) FOR GETTING TO SAINSBURY'S
AND BACK? IF SO WOULDN'T THE SIMPLEST THING BE FOR HER TO BUY A WATCH? BUT I DON'
T SUPPOSE SHE
COULD AFFORD THE TIME IT WOULD TAKE TO WALK TO THE JEWELLER'S. OH, DEAR. SHE WA
SN'T THERE TODAY. NOT THIS AFTERNOON NOR THIS MORNING. PERHAPS SHE'S LYING LOW
UNTIL THE FIRST REAL DAY OF SPRING. POOR WOMAN, HER SPRING IS OVER, SHE IS ON HER
LAST LEGS. DON'T GIVE UP, DEAR. OR RATHER, FEEL FREE TO GIVE UP, BUT ONLY IF YOU MU
ST. ENOUGH!... I BOUGHT THIS PEN FROM SMITH'S ON THE WAY BACK FROM THE COPIER. AN
D I REDID THE LAST LINE PRE-COPIER WITH THE NEW PEN TO SEE HOW IT LOOKED
AND BECAUSE I'D TAKEN UP TOO MUCH SPACE WITH MY FIRST EFFORT. WHO GIVES A FUCK?
I DO. I'M CREATING A VISUAL EVENT, A HORIZON FOCAL AREA A LA SEAN LANDERS. WHO GI
VES A FUCK? NOT EVEN ME. STOP FOR A MINUTE. EVERY FEW INCHES. OH,
DEAR. I'VE JUST NOTICED THAT MY LINES AREN'T STRAIGHT. I'VE REACHED FURTHER DOWN
THE RIGHT EDGE THAN THE LEFT. I'LL DO A LITTLE ADJUSTMENT RIGHT HERE AND TRY TO RE
MEMBER TO DO THE SAME FOR THE NEXT FEW LINES. THIS IS AN A3 SHEET OF MOUNTING
BOARD THAT I'M WRITING ON AND IT LOOKS GREAT EVEN WITH THE IMPERFECT LINES. PERH
APS I SHOULD HAVE USED A RULER (ADJUST.) BUT NO I THINK THIS IS GOING ALRIGHT AS IT IS.
IF THERE'S A PROBLEM - AND THERE'S BOUND TO BE A PROBLEM - IT'LL
BE IN THE CONTENT RATHER THAN THE FORM. I'M GOING TO TAKE THAT BREAK I MENTIONED
A COUPLE OF LINES UP. "YES, DO, DUNC, TAKE THAT BREAK. YOU DESERVE IT AFTER ALL T
HAT WRITING SOME OF WHICH IS NOT COMPLETELY SELF-CENTRED FOR A
WELCOME CHANGE. WHY NOT TAKE A SHOWER, EVEN? SHOWER, DUNC, SHOWER." 16.00...
THAT WAS HOPELESS. THERE MAY BE A BROKEN PIPE IN THE SHOWER UNIT. WHEN THE SH
OWER IS ON, COLD WATER STREAMS DOWN THE WALL. FUCKED TOILET, FUCKED SHOWER.
"IF I WERE A PLUMBER
BUT THEN AGAIN, NO." I'VE LEFT A NOTE DOWNSTAIRS FOR MY LANDLADY WHO WILL BE OVE
R THE MOON ABOUT THAT. BUT IF I DON'T LEAVE A NOTE AND SHE ENDS UP HAVING TO CALL
THE PLUMBER TWICE SHE MIGHT HOLD IT AGAINST ME. OH, WELL... ON SATURDAY, AFTER SE
EING
A COUPLE OF SHOWS, JOANNA AND I ARE GOING TO HER STUDIO SPACE AT CHELSEA TO LO
OK AT THE WORK SHE'S DOING FOR THE M.A. MID-YEAR SHOW. SHE'S GOT TWO LARGE (6' BY
4') PHOTOS, AND SHE NEEDS TO DECIDE IF SHE WANTS A THIRD PHOTO OR NEEDS TO PUT O
NE OR ALL
OF THE PHOTOS BEHIND 2-WAY GLASS. THAT SHOULD BE FUN, NOT LEAST BECAUSE I'M IN T
HE PHOTOS. NO, I DON'T MEAN THAT. I'M NOT VAIN. AND ANYWAY IT'S ONLY MY HANDS THAT A
RE IN SHOT. I'M STRANGLING THE POOR WOMAN. MY SELFISHNESS, MY OBSESSION WITH

MY WRITING AND MY DISINTERESTEDNESS (WRONG WORD) IN HER ART AND HER LIFE ARE CH
OKING THE LIFE OUT OF JOANNA. BUT I DON'T BELIEVE THAT AND NEITHER DOES JOANNA. I H
OPE. SHE FEELS THAT OUR RELATIONSHIP IS STRONGER THAN IT WAS SIX
MONTHS AGO AND THIS HAS GIVEN HER THE DISTANCE FROM THIS PIECE OF WORK TO COME
BACK TO IT WITH MORE CONFIDENCE. I THINK. ON SUNDAY WE WILL GO TO THE COUNTRY FO
R THE DAY, PROBABLY. WE WON'T IF I NEED TO BE HERE ON SUNDAY NIGHT SO AS
TO MAKE A FAST START ON MY WRITING ON MONDAY MORNING. BUT IF THIS WEEK'S WRITING
GOES WELL, IS EFFECTIVELY IN THE BAG BY SATURDAY MORNING, THEN FUCK IT - SHE CAN
HAVE ME ON SUNDAY NIGHT AS WELL! JUDY OVER THE
MOON ABOUT MY NOTE. JOANNA OVER THE MOON ABOUT US HAVING A WHOLE DAY TOGET
HER. I CERTAINLY KNOW HOW TO KEEP MY WOMEN IN ORBIT! OUT THERE IN SPACE - WHERE
NOBODY CAN HEAR YOU SCREAM. "TAKE ANOTHER BREAK, DUNC, YOU
DESERVE IT. READ THE PAPER THEN STUFF YOUR FUCKING FACE FULL OF FOOD. TRY NOT T
O CHOKE ON YOUR SELF-SATISFACTION. FUCKING CLOWN." 16.35... 17.59. I'VE EATEN AND I'
VE READ BUT NOT THE PAPER. I WENT BACK TO SEAN'S TEXT, FIRST TO THE CATALOGUE
ILLUSTRATION THOUGH NOT FOR LONG. I REALLY AM THROUGH WITH THAT MAGNIFYING GLA
SS. (HOW ARE YOU DOING? HA! YOU DON'T EXIST.) AND THEN TO THE LINES I TRANSCRIBED.
SEAN SAYS "FUCK YOU IF YOU HATE ME." BUT I DON'T HATE YOU SEAN. "REALLY, I WELCOME
YOUR HATRED.
I HATE YOU TOO." I STILL CAN'T HATE YOU SEAN. DO YOU HATE ME? DO YOU SEAN OR JOANN
A OR WHOEVER YOU ARE, HATE ME? SURELY NOT. LOVE ME, LOVE MY WORK. IF I CAN DO IT
SURELY YOU CAN. SEAN ASKS ME, "WHAT DO YOU DO THAT'S SO FUCKING GREAT?" THIS FO
R A
START. AND ALL DAY I'VE BEEN DOING THINGS THAT ARE SO FUCKING GREAT. I MADE THE CA
T PURR. I JUST LOOKED AT IT AND IT STARTED TO PURR. I STROKED IT AND IT SPRAYED ALL O
VER THE KITCHEN. JUST ONE OUT OF ABOUT A HUNDRED THINGS I'VE DONE
TODAY THAT'S SO FUCKING GREAT. I SHOULD N'T HAVE AVOIDED JAMES THOUGH. I SHOULD
HAVE WENT OUT WHEN HE WAS IN THE KITCHEN AND ASKED HIM HOW HIS NEW JOB WAS GOI
NG. "FINE, DUNC, FINE." AND WAS HE SETTLING INTO THE FLAT ALRIGHT? WELL
ACTUALLY, NO. HE'S NEVER BEEN SO LONELY AND DEPRESSED AND HE'S MOVING OUT AT T
HE WEEKEND. HE TOLD ME THAT EARLIER THIS WEEK. DON'T GIVE UP, JAMES. OR RATHER, F
EEL FREE TO GIVE UP, BUT ONLY IF YOU MUST. 18.20. THE LIBRARY CLOSES AT EIGHT
TONIGHT SO I'LL GET ONE MORE COPY DONE. IT MIGHT AS WELL BE NOW... IT'S NOT SO COLD
OUTSIDE THIS EVENING BUT IT IS DARK. ALL THE WAY TO THE LIBRARY AND BACK THAT ELTO
N JOHN SONG WAS GOING THROUGH MY MIND. "I HOPE YOU DON'T MIND, I HOPE YOU DON'T MI
ND, THAT I
PUT DOWN IN WORDS..." WHICH IS WHAT I GET FOR ENJOYING MY OWN JOKE. 'HOW WONDERF
UL LIFE IS WHILE YOU'RE IN THE WORLD.' PEOPLE ARE IN DOWNSTAIRS AND JAMES IS BACK
TOO. I ASKED HIM HOW HE WAS GETTING ON. HE'S GOT TO START HIS TRAINING COURSE AGA
IN WHEN HE
MOVES TO EAST LONDON. THE REPEAT OF THE HEALTH AND SAFETY LECTURES WILL PRO
BABLY BORE HIM TO DEATH - THEY BORED HIS BALLS RIGHT OFF THE FIRST TIME. BUT AT LE
AST THIS MEANS THAT HE WON'T HAVE TO TAKE PUBLIC TRANSPORT ALL THE WAY ACROSS
LONDON
JUST TO GET IN A BUS TO DO HIS DRIVING. JAMES IS IN A GOOD MOOD BECAUSE HE'S BEEN
TO SEE 'TRAINSPOTTING'. I'M IN A GOOD MOOD BECAUSE I'VE GOT THREE EXQUISITE PHOTO
COPIES NOW. NEEDLESS TO SAY IT'S 'TRAINSPOTTING' WE TALK ABOUT. CONGRATULATI ON
S
IRVINE WELSH... HOW DOES SEAN FINISH HIS TEXT AGAIN? 'I AM HERE NOW AND WILL NOT AL
WAYS BE.' SO VERY TRUE. TODAY'S BEEN GREAT. THE STRAWBERRY YOGHURT I ATE AT DIN
NER; THE SHOWER THAT WASN'T HOPELESS AT ALL ONCE I STOOD CLEAR OF THE COLD SPI
LL;
THE SOUND OF LELLHI LAUGHING AS SHE RAN UP THE STAIRS PURSUED BY JESS. AND IT'S
NOT OVER YET. I'VE MY CALL TO JOANNA TO LOOK FORWARD TO. AND I JUST MIGHT RISK TH
AT BOTTLE OF WINE THAT'S IN THE FRIDGE. I SAY RISK BECAUSE I DON'T
WANT TO FUCK UP MY LINES AT THIS STAGE. BUT WORTH RISKING, AS OMAR KHAYAM (SPEL
LING CHECK PLEASE, AND I'VE SPELT L'S NAME WRONG FOR SURE) FOR ONE WOULD TESTIF
Y. 20.02 AND ALL'S WELL WITH THE WORLD. I JUST WISH THAT ELTON
WOULD FUCK OFF OUT OF IT. ELTON: "IS THAT BETTER, DUNC?" YES, THAT'S QUIET, ELTON.
SEAN: "DUNC, ARE YOU SURE NOW?" JUST POUR OUT THE WINE, SEAN, LAD. CHEERS. I WOK

E UP JOANNA SO WE DIDN'T TALK FOR LONG, THE DOZY DUCK. "DUNC, I'M STILL SLEEPY," SH
E
KEPT SAYING. I MANAGED NOT TO TELL HER ABOUT TODAY. WITH ANY LUCK SHE'LL READ TH
IS AT THE WEEKEND - MY ONLY READER AND MY HARSHEST CRITIC. SHE HAD A TUTORIAL TO
DAY FROM HELEN CHADWICK WHICH SHE RECKONED USEFUL. I POOH-POOHED
THAT AND TOLD HER I'D SORT THINGS OUT FOR THE PIECE AT THE WEEKEND. (IF I WAS A SCU
LPTOR, BUT THEN AGAIN I AM.) "MORE WINE, DUNC?" NO SEAN, I WAS GOING TO POUR THE R
EST OF THE BOTTLE DOWN THE FUCKED TOILET TO SEE IF THAT WOULD DO THE
TRICK. (IF I WAS A PLUMBER, BUT THEN AGAIN I AM.) GOD, I FEEL GOOD. WILL THIS FEELING LA
ST? FOR MINUTES, DAYS, YEARS, THE REST OF MY LIFE? THAT KIND OF DEPENDS ON WHETH
ER I'M HIGH ON THIS TEXT - WHICH ALL MY LIFE I'VE BEEN
PREPARING FOR - OR WHETHER IT'S THE WINE. IN WHICH CASE THE FEELING WILL PASS. BUT
SO WHAT - THERE COULD BE (THERE WILL BE) ANOTHER BOTTLE TOMORROW. THE BOTTLE
WHICH IS STANDING ON MY TABLE TO THE
RIGHT OF MY WRITING BOARD AND NOW FAR TO THE RIGHT OF MY CRAWLING, SCRAWLING HA
ND WHICH IS EDGING CLOSER AGAIN TO THE WINE. BUT FORGET THE WINE, IT'S THE TEXT AND
TODAY THAT MATTER, ALL THE THINGS THAT
HAPPENED HAVE GONE INTO BOTH... I GOT UP AT 6.47. I HAD TO CLEAR DUST OFF THE BOAR
D. IT IS STRANGE THAT DUST SHOULD HAVE... PERHAPS I SHOULD HAVE FINISHED THIS LAST
NIGHT. BUT I DIDN'T WANT TO FORCE IT. AND I SUDDENLY GOT TIRED, SO I LEFT IT, DRANK THE
WINE (NOT TOO
TIRED FOR THAT) THEN WATCHED AN HOUR OF TV. THEN SLIPPED INTO BED. I HAVE NOTHING
TO SAY TODAY BUT I WILL SIT HERE UNTIL I GET TO THE END OF THE PAGE. KILLING SPACE. IS
THAT TRUE? HAVE I NOTHING TO SAY? IT'S A NEW DAY, SPARROWS
ARE CHIRPING AND THIS TEA IS GOOD AND HOT. NOTHING TO SAY. DID I EVER HAVE ANYTHING
TO SAY? WELL, DID YOU, DUNC? DID YOU EVER HAVE ANYTHING TO SAY ABOUT THE DRUDGE
RY OF WORK (OH, TH AT ACCOUNTANCY FIRM) OR THE JOYS OF CREATION (OH, ARCHIE,
BLESS YOU MY BOY, MY ALTAR EGO, MY SELF)? I'D LIKE TO THINK THAT THE ANSWER IS IN TH
E QUESTION. WOULD YOU, DUNC? WOULD YOU LIKE TO THINK THAT THE ANSWER IS IN THE Q
UESTION? WELL THAT'S HELL OF AN INTERESTING, HELL OF AN AMUSING,
AND KIND OF CONFIRMS YOU'VE GOT NOTHING TO SAY, AND NEVER DID HAVE. NEVER DID HA
VE ANYTHI NG TO SAY. I'M FORCING IT. KILLING SPACE. SEARCHING FOR THE END OF THE PA
GE. BUT IT'S NOT THERE YET. MORE TEA, VICAR?... FRIDAY, MARCH 8, 1996.
I'LL MAKE A FINAL PHOTOCOPY OF THIS PAGE (ONLY WHEN IT'S FINISHED) AND THEN I'LL RE-
DRAFT THE DIARY PART OF THE TEXT. SUNDAY IS OKAY. MONDAY AND TUESDAY NEED REST
RUCTURING. AND WEDNESDAY NEEDS FIRMING UP. IF I CAN TYPE THAT
IN THE AFTERNOON THEN FINE, I'LL DO THAT, SO JOANNA CAN READ THE TEXT THIS WEEKEN
D. WHAT A TREAT FOR HER!...NOTHING TO SAY... FRIDAY, MARCH 8... I SHOULD WASH MY CLO
THES AND CUT MY HAIR TODAY BUT THERE WON'T BE TIME. I SHOULD GO TO
THE OPTICIAN BUT I'VE BEEN GOING TO THE OPTICIAN EVERY WEEK FOR THE LAST THREE Y
EARS AND I STILL HAVEN'T GOT THERE. ACCORDING TO JOANNA MY GLASSES DON'T SUIT ME
. AND THE RIGHT LENS IS SCORED. BUT SO WHAT. IF USE OF THE MAGNIFYING
GLASS HAS TEMPORARILY AFFECTED THE BALANCE OF MY EYES THEN THIS WOULD BE A P
RETTY DAFT TIME TO GO TO THE OPTICIANS. GOD. THIS BLACK BORDER IS PLAYING HAVOC W
ITH MY SIGHT NOW. I'M SEEING A SIZZLING WHITE LINE WHEN I BLINK. IS THAT
THE NEGATIVE OF THE BLACK BORDER OR IS IT THE THICK WHITE LINE I'M CREATING BETWEE
N THIS WRI TING AND THE BLACK BORDER? HURRY UP AND FINISH THE PAGE. TODAY TO SAY. I
THINK IT WOULD BE A GOOD IDEA TO TAKE A LASER COPY OF THIS PAGE
SO THAT LAZY-EYED PEOPLE CAN SKIP THE ORDINARY COPIES AND DO THEIR LAZY EYES A
FAVOUR BY GOING STRAIGHT TO THE QUALITY COPY. BUT HOW WILL THEY KNOW TO DO THA
T? YOU WON'T TELL THEM, WILL YOU, DUNC? NOPE, I WON'T DO MY READERS ANY
FAVOURS IN THAT DIRECTION. THE ONLY FAVOUR I'M DOING THAT LOT IS WRITING OUT THIS T
EXT. WHAT MARVELLOUS STRAIGHT LINES! HOW DID YOU MANAGE THAT, DUNC? OH, YOU KN
OW, NATURAL TALENT AND HARD WORK. BUT I'LL REDUCE LETTER SIZE HERE
SO AS TO GET A FULL LAST LINE IN. LAST LINE. NOTHING TO SAY? TODAY TO SAY. I AM HERE
TODAY AND WON'T ALWAYS BE. A FUNNY FEELING IN MY STOMACH AND MY EYES. I AM HERE
TODAY AND WON'T ALWAYS BE. FUNNY FEELING. TODAY, YESTERDAY, TOMORROW.

PRET A MANGER

Duncan McLaren
Pret A Lire
51 Sunderland Road
Forest Hill
London   SE23 2PS

Dear Duncan McLaren

Interesting ring binders. Challenging text.

Yours sincerely

Julian Metcalfe
CHAIRMAN

11 March 1996

DIRECT LINE: 0171 827
Old Mitre Court 43 Fleet Street London EC4Y 1BT
Telephone 0171 827 6300 ★ Facsimile 0171 827 6333

DIRECTORS: J E METCALFE   S C S BEECHAM . PRET A MANGER (EUROPE) LTD . REGISTERED IN ENGLAND REG. N? 1854213

I WENT TO A SHOW
BY
ROBERTA & BOB SMITH
AND ALL I GOT
WAS THIS 'CHALLENGING
TEXT'.

POSTSSSSS Total Charge £10.00

Your patron number is

DUNCAN W. MCLAREN

10194080710717080077400000000

12-MAR-96

15
Day
Psycho

Day 1, Tuesday

To 'Spellbound' at the Hayward. Ten artists and film-makers show work exploring the affinity between art and film. I buy a season ticket because I have a hunch that Douglas Gordon's *24-Hour Psycho* will have to be seen more than once...

By silencing and slowing down Hitchcock's film (to a thirteenth of its original speed; three frames a second) strange things happen. First, the screen can be read like a painting or a still photograph. And since the director has arranged each frame carefully, there is much to be enjoyed from such a reading. Second, the mind is free to roam not only across the picture – to the most incidental parts of the frame – but also associatively and imaginatively, knowing that when it comes back to the screen nothing of the action has been lost. Third, what on earth have I been watching? I sat for half an hour and saw a scene which amounted to a film in itself. An experience I twice repeated in the course of the afternoon. And I'll be back tomorrow to see, I expect, completely different films. The mind boggles happily. Spellbound indeed.

Day 2, Wednesday

I slip into the Hayward and seconds later am staring up at the huge *Psycho* screen. An attractive young woman – I didn't see her yesterday – is standing outside a room, on a porch, in the dark.

Once my eyes have adjusted to the dim light of the gallery, I pick out an empty bean-bag and sit down on it. I look up. Tall, dark-haired Anthony Perkins appears carrying a tray with a white jug. He stops in front of Janet Leigh. Strong composition: his head (top left), her head (right), with between them at his waist/her chest level the well-rounded, starkly white jug which has just got to be full of milk. Thick, creamy milk.

Looking at the jug, not at her, he opens and closes his mouth and eyes; while she stares composedly into his eyes: two minutes. Then she opens and closes her mouth, her eyebrows raised and her eyes wide open, switching her gaze between the jug and his eyes; while he stares, inscrutably, into her eyes: two minutes. He mouths again, his eyes intent on the jug as before... but my eyes move around. I can't help noticing how good-looking she is. I pay serious attention to her breasts in particular, the roundness of which is echoed in her shoulder blades. I didn't know they had Wonderbras in 1960. But clearly they had Wonderbras and Wonderbra ads: 'Is that a pistol in your pocket or are you just blah, blah, blah?' She crosses her arms underneath her breasts and takes a backward step.

Front view of him, his eyes in shadow, his forehead creasing, as he hesitates. Front view of her, face severe, arms emphatically crossed, as she stands her ground. Stands her ground... He turns and walks away, the two unused glasses on his tray catching the light as he does so.

I go upstairs to sit among the people queuing for the Damien Hirst film, because it's light there and I can write this down in note form. But I'll be back.

•

Anthony Perkins – tall, dark and shifty-looking – is sitting in front of a piece of furniture on which stands a candlestick. The camera is looking up at him. He is leaning forward, forearms resting on thighs, hands clasped, fingers interlocking but constantly on the move... His Adam's apple comes and goes, rises and falls, and my attention is divided between that and those long, furtive fingers – that nest of snakes.

Fade to her: Janet Leigh. I look at the way her eye sockets, her cheekbones and her jaw define the shape of her face. She has a long neck, though the high-collared top she's wearing tempers this strong feature. And what big white eyes: the whitest things on the screen. I suppose the camera picks up extra light reflected by the thin film of liquid that covers the eyeball... I've no idea where this scene is taking place or how much time has elapsed between this and the last scene I saw, but the tray is now on the table at which she's sitting.

Him again. He's wearing a confident expression. His mouth is set in a grin as he opens and closes it, but who could trust that Adam's apple? That nest of snakes.

She takes a slice of bread into her hand and slowly butters it with a knife. Slowly butters it. Maybe margarine was invented then – though not Olivio or I Can't Believe It's Not Butter – but I assume it's butter. She tears the buttered bread in two, then sits still, listening to him, her elbow resting on the tabletop, her neat wrist leading to her delicate hand holding the bread in slim fingers in front of her mouth. She appears to blow on the bread, looking past it. She keeps blowing, staring in his direction. Oh, those cheekbones.

He extends a long arm behind him to what appears to be a stuffed bird beside the candlestick on top of the cabinet. And he mouths with an excited brightness as she continues to pose and to pout and to blow on the slice of bread still poised in front of her luscious mouth. Suddenly he stands up. The camera is looking sharply up at his head and shoulders, his thrusting Adam's apple all the more noticeable. Behind him, two 'flying' stuffed owls cast dark shadows on to the ceiling. She is eating the bread now – chewing it thoroughly – her lips moving, the curve of her cheeks coming and going, her eyes now wide open, now lidded and lashed. He looks upwards, blinking slowly, then looks her way again. Another morsel is sensuously swirled round her mouth. He opens and closes his mouth. I have to remind myself that he's talking. What is he saying so intensely, so desperately? 'I can't believe... it's not...' She goes on chewing and giving him the eye, 'I can't believe... it's not...' The sequence goes on and on.

Finally she drops her elegant arm and replaces the remaining crust on her plate. She looks at him severely. What does she say? 'I've been blowing you for twenty minutes and you still haven't come. *Do you have a problem or what?*' He blinks slowly – near orgasm, surely – and says (the owls displaying their maximum wingspan; his Adam's apple never more prominent), 'Not butter! Not butter! I just cannot believe it's not butter!'

Day 3, Thursday

Write up Day 2 in detail, so I don't get to London Bridge until mid-afternoon. I walk along the south bank of the Thames, past the reconstruction of Shakespeare's Globe (nearly thatched), past the Tate's brick Bankside (conversion not visibly started), to the Hayward in all its (here and now) concrete glory. I enter in time to catch *Psycho*'s opening scene. A stark modernist cityscape which the camera takes minutes to pan across; an open window which the camera takes minutes to zoom in on and through; an intimate, semi-naked couple, presumably post-coital... It takes her an age to button her blouse. I keep thinking she's going to change her mind but, no, the pushed-up and separated ones are being put away for the time being. The. Time. Being.

Day 4, Friday

No time to write up Day 3, but I do have half an hour to look in on *Psycho*. The shower scene: poor Janet. The naked woman is stabbed through the shower curtain, and doesn't the director just love it. Close-up of her screaming mouth, the water dripping from the bright enamel of her teeth. The scene ends with her pulling down the shower curtain on top of herself; the camera zooming in on the plughole down which the blood-clouded water disappears; zooming out again from the pupil of the dead girl's eye to show her lying with her face pressed against the tiled floor... I hurry off to Chelsea to help Joanna black out her space for the forthcoming mid-year show, but she has mismeasured the room and doesn't have sufficient material. She is distraught... And the rain, it raineth every day.

Day 5, Saturday

Joanna still stressed. She goes off to buy more material while I return to *Psycho*. It's the same scene as I saw on Day 2 – woman eating bread in front of fruitcake – so I go to the café upstairs, drink a coffee and read from the catalogue. When I come back the scene has not changed at all! I stand there aghast – I have completely lost the pace of the film.

Day 6, Sunday

Psycho: I make myself sit in front of the screen for half an hour, but I don't get a lot out of it. At home I phone Joanna. She has sewn on the extra material and is grateful to me for volunteering to help her again tomorrow.

Day 7, Monday

I stop off at *Psycho*. It is the final scene, in which a dejected Perkins sits in a cell, wrapped in a blanket, his long white hand protruding from the cloth like a knife... Out to Chelsea, where Joanna and I succeed in erecting the blackout. But not before I cause her electric drill to drop from the stepladder on to the floor, after which it won't work. She doesn't blame me for this, but I do. What a moron.

Day 8, Tuesday

The plan was for me to write, but I can't leave Joanna in the lurch. We spend the day blocking in two projectors and pinning the two four feet by seven feet photos to the walls in various conjunctions. On my way home, I drop into the Hayward, but I don't stay because I've seen the scene before and, anyway, I'm not in the mood. Someone has written in the visitors' book, '*Psycho* is a joke – I lasted 15 seconds.' And that is about what I've – temporarily, I hope – been reduced to.

Day 9, Wednesday

Didn't go to Chelsea – Joanna assures me she can manage on her own now, and thanks me for my help. Didn't go to *Psycho* – I didn't feel like it. Didn't write up my *Psycho* days to date – I didn't feel like that either... Am I going to lose this piece?

Day 10, Thursday

Didn't work.

Day 11, Friday

Can't work. Joanna's private view goes well – she gets positive feedback from colleagues and friends.

Day 12, Saturday

What is my problem?

Day 13, Sunday

My problem: it is going to be too TIME-CONSUMING to go back and flesh out the bones of my notes for Day 3 onwards. DEAD BORING. So what do I do?

Day 14, Monday

Pay a surprise visit to Joanna's installation, only it's Joanna's installation that surprises me. I take in the large photos on opposite walls as if for the first time. A man's hands around his own gigantic penis or a woman's neck? The projectors float more such images on top of the photos (one frame every two seconds), creating a hand-on-hand effect which softens the impact of the whole. I pass across the projector beams and my shadow is cast on to both photos, implicating me in the imagery... Not that I need implicating – these are my hands wrapped around Joanna's neck after all. She had to persuade me to put my hands round her throat. She had to insist on me exerting pressure on her neck to make the shots more realistic. As soon as she coughed or squirmed I would instantaneously release my grip whether she'd operated the shutter release or not. The situation disturbed me then – the possibility of my hurting her. The situation disturbs me now. Why? – I have not harboured a violent thought towards a woman in my life. That's unequivocal enough. Yet I am disturbed. Is it the sex-object angle? I do see women as sex objects in fantasies. I've looked upon Joanna that way before; of course I have. So I'm guilty of something then. No, not *guilty* exactly. What then? I'm not sure...

Day 15, Tuesday

I can finish this now. By writing up the scene I sat through – but didn't engage with at the time – on Day 6.

A stranger is 'talking' to Anthony Perkins outside the motel office. Perkins is eating popcorn out of a box which he offers to the stranger. Offer declined. The stranger asks about the girl and of course Perkins – open and relaxed – knows nothing about her...   No, that's wrong. The stranger doesn't mention the girl at this stage. Instead he tries to get a general feel for the place and for Perkins – too insouciant by half.

The two men have strikingly different physiques. The

stranger is squat, stocky, bull-necked and bulbous-nosed. He makes me doubt the qualities of Perkins's body. Isn't he too tall, too pale, too thin? Both those noses can't be right! Isn't Perkins's nose too long and pointed? Look how solid and dependable the stranger is (hits every woman like a sock on the jaw). And look what a long streak of misery Perkins is (breaks down and cries).

I get up from my writing table long enough to raise the needle from *Young Americans* – which is about to become distracting – and to switch off the record player.

The detective (hits every woman like a sock on the jaw... shit!) follows Perkins into the motel office and their slo-mo relationship resumes. The blunt cop shows Perkins a photo of the girl. Perkins takes it in the long fingers of his lilywhite hand and stares at it in all innocence – his jaw working on the popcorn as he does so – then hands back the picture with turns of his head to left and right. Perkins has never seen the girl before, never mind rented her a room for the night; Perkins has never laid eyes on her before, never mind ogled her from top to pretty bottom; Perkins doesn't know the girl from Eve, never mind showered with her in the bloody Garden of Eden.

Perkins turns aside, stretches out an arm and throws a switch. Outside, the neon sign lights up the words BATES MOTEL and VACANCY. In my opinion Perky is giving himself away, but all the tec sees is that little switch being thrown. Perky throws the switch again (why not – he's got so much time) and the word MASTER comes on in front of BATES and NO in front of VACANCY. MASTER BATES MOTEL, NO VACANCY. Perky smiles at his smutty joke as he flicks the switch for a third time, causing all the lights to go out as those on another circuit come on: WHAT A DUMB COP. Perky's smile widens in the knowledge that he can run rings round this dope.

Where was I? Oh, yes... The detective must request the hotel register, because Perkins produces it and lays it in front of his interlocutor. The tec slowly – with ponderous deliberation – turns the pages until he gets to the fateful day. His stubby finger rests on the paper underneath an entry written in a woman's hand, which reads, 'Psycho is a joke – he lasted 15 seconds.' The sentence stays on screen for two full minutes. Plenty time for the tec to consider it from every conceivable angle. What does it mean? Is it a clue? Will it mark a turning point in the clueless detective's investigation? Well, let's see...

The tec's face hardens. He doesn't want to do this – he's a decent guy. But he's a decent guy second and a good cop first. He's a faithful husband third, a decent guy second and a bloody good cop first. He's a randy so-and-so fourth, a faithful husband third, a decent guy second and one fuck of a good cop first and foremost. Get on with it. Staring assessingly into Perkins's eyes, he asks, 'How do you feel about oral sex? Is coming in a woman's mouth good for the ozone layer? Or is it bad, bad, bad for global warming?'

'It's bad, bad, bad...' Perky starts to reply, before deciding to cool it. He puts a thoughtful expression on his face then tries again. 'Coming in a woman's mouth is necessary and sufficient to prevent the build-up of plaque, thereby providing the best protection against gum disease. Coming in a woman's mouth is necessary but not by itself sufficient – some sort of concerted international action will also be required – to halt global warming. And coming in a woman's mouth is, in general, a hip, hip, hip thing to do.'

Not totally reassured by this answer (for some reason), the detective presents the snapshot for reappraisal. Perky doesn't even look at it as he denies all knowledge. The tec keeps the photo stuck out there, while explaining that it excludes her breasts and is therefore a poor likeness. The mental picture that Perky should be considering is a particular Wonderbra poster in which the very full-frontal model – lifted and separated – is saying, 'Party? Great! Mind if I bring a couple of friends along?'

Perkins is wearing his 'what a dumb cop' expression as he rotates his neck first one way then the other. But perhaps it's Perky that's the dumb one, dropping his guard, because he appears totally dumbfounded by the next question.

'What does your mother think about you shooting off in pretty girls' mouths?'

'Pardon me?' answers Perkins, the knob in his throat suddenly engorging, giving me time to admire the excellent police work. It reminds me of Robbie Coltrane in *Cracker*, this psychological hounding.

'What does your old lady think about blonde actresses sucking you off... giving head until the cows come home for milking... deep-throating you until the chickens come home to roost...'

Silence. Giving me time to admire again the still exemplary police work. As in *Cracker*, a programme I stopped watching on the grounds of quality control: gratuitous violence.

Finally Perkins (breaks down and cries) settles down enough to answer: 'Granted, my mother may have had her views on such a matter, but I for one was never made party to them.' Perkins looks pleased with his response. But he must know he's lost an awful lot of ground to his interrogator in recent exchanges. So he decides – perhaps unwisely – to continue: 'However, I think it's safe to say that mother would choke on her evening milk, if she thought... (Adam's apple bobbing)... if she thought for one minute... (Adam's apple trampolining)... if it crossed her mind for one banana sundae... (Adam's apple bungee-jumping)...'

Perky is there for the taking. Tec's big hands are wrapped around his throat. Tec's got the choice of choking the life out of the pervert or pushing his thumbs straight through the windpipe and into the Adam's apple... But what's this? A frown of uncertainty suggests that he thinks he's got the wrong man (me, perhaps); a pursing of lips suggests that this case is going to be a hard nut to crack after all.

Perky can't move except for one hand, which he and I move to a switch. WHAT A DUMB COP shines forth. Tec relaxes his grip on our throats. DUMB, DUMBER, DUMBEST. He goes away. VACANCY.

He goes away! I think he gets killed in the next scene. What next scene – there is no next scene. I'm tired. Finished. Good.

VACANCY

what did the spider say
to the fly?

what did the fly say
in return?

Duncan McLaren
51 Sunderland Rd.
LONDON SE 23 2PS.

Alfred Hitchcock
Psycho (Psychose), Alfred Hitchcock, 1960
Droits réservés
Éditions Hazan, Paris 1996

Postcard from Douglas Gordon

What did the spider say
to the fly?

VACANCY

What did the fly say in return?

You have got to be
fucking joking, darling.

27 March

I'd like to place an article in the summer issue of *Untitled*. This month's writing on Sean Landers and Douglas Gordon isn't suitable, too much about my reaction to their art rather than the art itself: not a review at all. There's another show at Anthony Wilkinson's which I want to visit, so maybe I'll be able to channel my thoughts about that into something suitably constrained. We'll see...

There's a painting on the wall.

There's a printed page on the wall, attached by a couple of nails through the paper's top corners. The paperback-sized page 59 *is* from a book judging by the torn left edge and the fact that lifting the bottom edge reveals page 60 on the reverse. The words on 59 have been deleted by black hatching except for a single sentence which reads: 'There's a painting on the wall.'

And indeed the only other object on display is a Peter Doig painting on an adjoining wall. A white wooden house or cabin is situated behind a lake and in front of woodland. The habitation is reflected in the water so that if the picture was turned upside-down the composition would hardly change. On the bank of the lake a figure has been roughly sketched, or is it a water pump? This doesn't feature in the reflection and adds a puzzling touch to an already enigmatic scene.

The deleted words of the page are just legible. A visitor has entered a room that has a very different picture on display – a classical allegory with Latin text – though that room too has otherwise bare white walls and parquet flooring like the one I'm standing in. There is a view down over districts of

Copenhagen from the large, bright room. 'The light of the winter morning comes in through the window, as white as if we were outside.' This takes me back to the landscape: from the raised porch that runs the length of the grand cabin there must be a fine view of trees and water... Text and image taken together are reminiscent of Doig's 1993/94 pictures which show a white block of flats (Le Corbusier's *Unité d'Habitation*) largely obscured by dark trees in its wild, wooded setting.

In the deleted text a conversation takes place between the visitor and the flat's owner: the inconvenient time of the visit is raised; a tragic accident is referred to; the sanctity of marriage is mentioned... I am about to run through this again when Anthony Wilkinson pops in for a chat about the work: Matthew Higgs asked Peter Doig to produce a painting in response to his amended text; the project could be repeated in collaboration with another painter; the page is from Peter Hoeg's novel *Miss Smilla's Feeling for Snow* – a prize-winning, detective story of literary merit which the dealer hasn't read.

Exploring the affinity between literature and art: Allan Rupensburg painted the text of *The Picture of Dorian Gray* over twenty-odd large canvases; Joseph Beuys filled six notebooks with drawings and watercolours for James Joyce's *Ulysses* extended by two chapters; Critical Decor displayed a photograph of themselves alongside an extract from Nietzsche's *Ecce Homo*... But it's not 'high' literature that Matthew Higgs mainly deals with. Earlier book-page pieces were sourced from crime novels or romantic fiction. Reading such books, the artist searched for – or tripped over – references to painting, which he then drew attention to through his work. An element of mockery was involved, though the principal target – the book's characters, the book's normal readership or the artist himself – depended on the particular reference highlighted and its context.

In *(Total) Despair*, each page of the Nabokov novel *Despair* was pinned to a gallery wall, words deleted in the same way as on the single page here. And as here a single passage was left alone. I ask Anthony Wilkinson what those lines were, but he can't recall. Disingenuous of me, because I know that they concluded,

'If some good soul helped me to arrange an exhibition, next day I'd be famous and rich.'

I doubt if this memory lapse on the part of his dealer would bother Matthew Higgs though, since the present work was sold inside a week to a New York collector. Richer and better known! And so what if the good soul who helped to arrange the exhibition has forgotten the first thing about the last one?

Anthony remains standing beside me, looking thoughtful. He thinks he *can* remember the surviving sentence from *(Total) Despair*. He thinks it read, 'If I was a sculptor, but then again no.' I point out that this is a line from an Elton John song. The line crops up (amongst hundreds on non-Elton John lines, it has to be said) in the text painting, *For Love of Nothing* by Sean Landers, recently displayed in 'Young Americans' at Saatchi's. So I can quite understand how the mistake has arisen.

Anthony is still looking pensive. Suddenly he brightens: he *knows* he can remember the surviving sentence. It read, 'Spontaneously I slip off my shoes.' I frown and peer at the page on the wall, and point out that this sentence is a deleted line from the present text. Anthony accepts this, apologizes for his error, explains that he's been poring over that particular page for too long recently and asks me to bear with him as he slips off to his office for a moment...

He comes back with his own copy of *Miss Smilla's Feeling for Snow*, a pristine Flamingo paperback. He turns to page 59, which is not so pristine – a mess of deletions, Tippexed deletions of deletions, and black-ink reinstatement of deletions (deletions of deletions of deletions). I notice that all the words on the page have finally been struck out in the manner of his artist. 'Look again,' Anthony urges. Sure enough, the last sentence is extant: 'I am the bride of Jesus.'

On the way home I buy a copy of the book, wondering what line will jump out at me when I see the untouched, printed page 59. 'Nothing else is needed.' I delete the rest of the page and spend the afternoon interacting with the novel in a more conventional way.

By the time I get to the end of page 171 I realize I've been a bit hasty. So I go into town again to try and exchange the book. 'On what grounds?' asks the assistant. I tell her I'm not happy about page 59. She turns to it and asks if I made the marks. I suggest that Messrs Higgs/Doig/Wilkinson are jointly responsible. She asks me again if I made the marks. I say something about a tragic accident and the sacred nature of creativity... but she won't buy it. So I have to.

My second till receipt of the day shows that at 19.11 on 28 March I rendered £6 for MISS SMILLA'S FE and was given £0.01 change. Home, I remove page 59 with some difficulty from the surprisingly robust volume and delete the text in a now familiar manner... Leaving me to admire the ultimate one-liner, which simultaneously celebrates, ridicules and epitomizes today's collaborations. I'm not sure how he does it, but Anthony Wilkinson does have a knack of arriving at aesthetically optimal solutions:

She looks at the letter I stuck through the door. It's the letter to Juliane about her being awarded a pension.

"I remember this letter quite well," she says.

There's a painting on the wall. From the heavens, down towards the earth, flows a stream of long-bearded patriarchs, fat little children, fruit, cornucopias, hearts, anchors, royal crowns, cannons, and a text you can read if you know Latin. This picture is the only sign of luxury. Other than that, the room has bare white walls, a parquet floor with wool carpets, an oak desk, a low, round table, a pair of high-backed chairs, a sofa, a tall bookcase, and a crucifix.

Nothing else is needed. Because there is something else here. A view that only a pilot would normally see, tolerable provided you don't suffer from vertigo. The apartment seems to consist mainly of one very large, bright room. Over by the balcony, along the entire width of the room, there is a wall of glass. From there you can see all of Frederiksberg, Bellahøj, and, in the distance, Høje Gladsaxe. The light of the winter morning comes in through the window, as white as if we were outside. On the other side there is another large window. From there you can see the spires of Copenhagen, across an endless expanse of rooftops. High above the city, Elsa Lübing and I stand as if in a bell jar, trying to size each other up.

She offers me a hanger for my coat. Spontaneously I slip off my shoes. Something about the room demands it. We sit down in two high-backed chairs.

"This time of day," she says, "I am normally at prayer."

She says this as naturally as if she were usually in the middle of the heart association's exercise programme at this time of day.

"So – unwittingly – you have chosen an inconvenient time," she says.

"I saw your name on the letter and looked you up in the phone book."

She looks at the paper again. Then she takes off her thick-lensed reading glasses.

"A tragic accident. Especially for the child. A child needs both parents. That is one of the practical reasons why marriage is sacred."

"Mr Lübing would be pleased to hear that."

If her husband is dead, I'm not insulting anyone. If he's alive, it's a tasteful compliment.

"There is no Mr Lübing," she says. "I am the bride of Jesus."

59

●

I'm wondering if John Stathatos will print my review (if some good soul would consistently publish my work, sooner or later I'd be famous and rich), but I doubt it somehow.

Anthony Wilkinson and John Stathatos are standing together. 'I am the bride of Satan,' says the dealer. The editor shakes his head firmly, and gently points out the limitations of such a statement – its fundamental lack of utility. Changing the subject, Stathatos mentions that he has read the Peter Hoeg novel. The first half of the book is excellent – fascinating protagonist, unfamiliar setting and an all-round vitality – but in the second half all that vitality seeps away with the change of location from Copenhagen to an Arctic-going ship. From literary thriller to page-turner full stop. He can quite see why Books Etc. refer to MISS SMILLA'S FE on their till receipts...

Wilkinson hears him out, then asserts, 'I am the bride of Satan's doppelgänger.' Stathatos frowns fiercely, opens his mouth as if to speak, but closes it again without doing so, as if thinking better of it. He turns towards me with eyebrows raised and asks me to intercede on sanity's behalf. I raise my arms aloft – like a cormorant drying its wings, perhaps – and announce: 'I AM THE BRIDE OF SATAN'S DOPPELGÄNGER'S HUGGER-MUGGER.'

9th April 1996

350 SAUCHIEHALL STREET
GLASGOW G2 3JD
TEL +44 (0)141 332 7521
FAX +44 (0)141 332 3226

CCa

Duncan McLaren
51 Sunderland Rd.
Forest Hill
London SE23 2PS

Dear Mr McLaren,

Thank you very much for taking the trouble to send us your
response to the Dalziel and Scullion exhibition. I really enjoyed
reading it, and have now passed it on to Matthew and Louise.

I can't help wondering whether the pheasant survived.

Yours sincerely,

Nicola White
Exhibitions Director

Centre for Contemporary Arts is a company limited by guarantee
with charitable status, registered in Scotland No. 140944.
Subsidised by the Scottish Arts Council and Glasgow City Council.

4 East Street, St. Combs, Aberdeenshire AB43 5YX
15th April 1996.

Dear Duncan McLaren,

We were recently forwarded your writing on wings, bird watching, running over a pheasant and reflections on Sainsbury's sausages. It was most considerate of you to think of responding to our work in this way, and we should like to thank you for taking the time to do so. We wish you many more reflective + enlightened moments in your observation of birds. You may be interested to know that there are some very good birds (similar to those you described) close to where we live on the edge of the Loch of Strathbeg. Our show at Glasgow is apparently on at the Ikon in Birmingham and will then go on to the Arnolfini in Bristol in June. Thanks again for sending us your writing which we very much enjoyed.

Best wishes
Matthew Dalziel and
Louise Scullion.

Matthew Dalziel and Louise Scullion
4 East Street
St. Combs
Aberdeenshire AB43 5YX

Duncan McLaren
51 Sunderland Road
London SE23 2PS

Tel. 0181 291 6979

25 April, 1996

Dear Matthew and Louise,

Thanks for the postcard. You are right in thinking that I am a keen
bird watcher. So when I heard there were rare migrant ducks in your
area I headed north. Eagerly.

Perhaps I should have gone by train. Certainly I had problems with
the car journey. Pheasants seem drawn to my front bumper these days,
and by the time I'd crossed the border - despite braking and swerving
to avoid such incidents - I'd clunked five cocks. I was driving
along with my head full of misgivings, and the car boot full of dead
birds in all their breeding-season finery.

By slowing to a cruising speed of 20 miles an hour, I thought I'd dealt
with the problem. And although this led to a queue of traffic building
up behind me, so it seemed. Then I heard a bump from the back of the
car. I stopped, considered the dead pheasant on the road, and calculated
that it must have waited until the front wheels passed (in other words,
until it was out of my field of vision) before throwing itself under the
car in the path of the inside back wheel. Clever little devil. I put him
with the others and became aware of... cacophony. Several of the cars
behind me were tooting their horns, indignant that I'd taken the innocent
creature's life. "What more could I have done? What more can I do?" I
asked the driver of the nearest vehicle, offering her a cube of tofu with
a green fruit-gum embedded in it. "Thank you so much for stopping completely,
but would you soon resume your journey," said the woman, who'd been very
patient with me for a hundred miles but was clearly anxious to be gone
from the site of the calamity.

I speeded up after that, took not a blind bit of notice of various clunks and bumps, and arrived at the Loch of Strathbeg with an hour of daylight remaining. Inside the hide (just like the one on the River Tay) were a couple of twitchers, binoculars intent on the water. I sat down between them and raised my glasses as the woman on the left said, "I think it's a Bob and Roberta Smith Duck, I really do." From my right the man's voice said, "Yes. The female. A small, pied duck, with pin tail, golden eye, and a characteristic toss of the head. What a positive I.D.!"

"Oh, fuck off," I said. Perhaps too loudly for the small hut, because I could sense both of my fellow enthusiasts removing their eyes from their optical instruments and turning to stare in my direction. Softly, I went on. "Look at the quiff. Look at those sideburns... That's Elvis or I'm a Dutchman." They trained their binoculars onto the loch again.

"I think you're right," said the bloke. "How unusual. The Elvis Presley Lesser Spotted Merganser."

"No, no, no... Elvis himself. He's either swimming or he's walking in a shallow part of the loch. By the angle of his neck I'd say it must be the latter. Elvis Presley. I'd always wondered whether he'd survived. I'd never believed those statistics about how much he was eating. 97,000 calories per day! That's a lot of British mice, I can tell you... Anyway, now I know - he survived. Now we all know - he pulled through... Listen! - he's singing. Do you recognise the song?"

"I aint nuthin but a hound-dog," said the man. Her partner adding, "Sniffin' after you."

I ran out of the hut and down to the shore. "Elvis, do you do requests?" A flock of ducks exploded from the surface of the loch. But that was alright, Elvis was still there. "Will you sing for me......" and to my embarrassment I couldn't think of a single Elvis Presley number. To be honest, I could never understand what the fuss had been about; I'd never been a fan. By the time the phrase 'Heartbreak Hotel' came to mind, Elvis had dived. There wasn't a sign of life on the water. Not a mallard.

Silence. Except for raucous rumblings from the hide behind me. My fellow twitchers, upset perhaps that Elvis hadn't stayed for an encore. Oh, Elvis, will you never be done with letting people down. Letting people down and pissing them around...

Anyway, I'm back in London now, on the look-out for more rare and wonderful exhibitions. Enclosed is a list of artists whose work I've written about recently.

Thank-you again for acknowledging my text.

Best wishes,

Duncan McLaren.

ENTITLED

Charing Cross Road. I can see the new edition of *Untitled* through bookshop window. The front cover is a still from Douglas Gordon's *24-Hour Psycho*. But it's what's inside that matters to me.

I don't like this particular shop but I am eager to see my name in print. So I step inside long enough to make the transaction. Outside again, I open up the broadsheet. The Bob and Roberta Smith review is credited to David McLaren on the contents page; and David McLaren is the name at the foot of the review on page 12. I place the journal in my bag and walk away.

I should have seen this coming. I did see it coming: twice. The other night I dreamt that John Stathatos, editor of *Untitled*, was showing me a messily pasted-up proof of the journal with the name Duncan Miles credited to my review. I pointed out the error and was told not to worry; the editor simply had to flick a switch and he could have any name in the phone directory. So that was all right. But I must have stared at the misnomer intently because it was a clear image when I awoke, and it has remained with me since.

Then this morning there was a cheque for thirty pounds from *Untitled*. John Stathatos had signed the cheque twice. Once in the usual place and once where he'd deleted his own handwritten 'David' and replaced it with 'Duncan'. My only thought at the time was what a nice little surprise – we hadn't discussed payment for my contribution.

Cork Street. I'm not going to be able to concentrate on exhibitions, but I'll wander into Entwistle's anyway. Work by Edward Lipski. A simple text piece catches my eye: an array of nine boxes which light up singly and consecutively, to read:

Today   is   Thursday

and   it   is

warm   and   sunny

I place my bag on the floor. As the sequence starts again I mentally correct it where necessary:

Today   is   Tuesday

and   it   is

warm   and   drizzly

I say this aloud in the empty gallery, in time with the boxes lighting up again. The woman behind the desk tells me that a couple came in on a bright Thursday and admired the piece. But when they revisited – on a cold and wet Monday – they were disappointed that the work hadn't changed. I smile, say a few words back, and for some reason she asks me my name.

Today	is	Tuesday
and	it	is
David	not	Duncan

Tuesday	not	Thursday
drizzly	not	sunny
David	not	Duncan

But I manage to answer her as if today had never happened:

Duncan	is	Duncan
and	it	is
warm	and	sunny

Suddenly I do feel in the mood for gallery bashing. I pick up my bag and get on with it...

Over lunch I read *Untitled*. Stathatos has edited my piece well: he's tightened it up by omitting the paragraphs I included on the video *Humiliate*, which wasn't in the show; and he has left alone the last section, the report of my own experience with the work, my participation.

This is good news. It makes me hopeful that Stathatos will be sympathetic to the equally subjective element in the review of Matthew Higgs's work that I'm about to send him. He might even print it. Especially if my covering letter communicates my disappointment upon reading 'David' in front of 'McLaren' at the end of the Bob and Roberta review. Be subtle, Dunc; don't overdo it, and don't explicitly link error with redress.

Shall I claim that I have a brother called David, a big *News of the World* reader, from whom I'm estranged, to whom I owe a lot of money and who hates my university-educated guts? Or shall I claim that I have a brother David, recently deceased, whose promising career in the visual arts was tragically cut short when a concrete aeroplane fell on to his head from a glass shelf in the ICA, and whose name moves me to tears every time I set eyes on it? No and no.

I head off to Anthony Wilkinson's gallery. I intend to let him see the Higgs review before I send it to *Untitled*. Why? The dealer may take exception to the way I've portrayed him, even if it is so obviously a fiction. But the fact is I'd like to get his reaction to it. And even if *Untitled* print the piece, I'd have to wait three months for that and for any response.

Besides, it's only fair. Anthony has let me into his flat to see the shows he's put on. He's trusted me, if you like. And he did seem anxious that my article on Bob and Roberta didn't mention the name of the artist who crops up several times on the video soundtrack. Twice he asked me not to disclose her name. So he may be equally sensitive about his own name being bandied about. Particularly if he feels I'm sullying his professional reputation. 'Anthony, what's in a name?' I'll ask him, if need be. But if he really would prefer to hide under a pseudonym then I'll see what John Stathatos can come up with. David Davidson?

Great Ormond Street. Anthony takes my review, but is too busy with something else to read it while I am looking at the present show. I feel I've lost the initiative here, but what can I do? Nothing. He retreats into his office, leaving me to take in Nicky Hirst's work.

A black cord across the doorway prevents access to the main room, where there is a stainless-steel, castor-wheeled trolley. On its lower level there is a pile of neatly folded, pristine white towels; some crisply folded white linen on which rest two white cards with strings attached – like luggage tags; a roll of white swaddling and a kidney-shaped, stainless-steel dish. On the top level rest two bowls of water, a brush, wads of cotton wool, three cotton plugs and three more kidney-shaped dishes – one with scissors and another with elastoplast. The work is called *Trolley for the Last Offices*, and what I thought was a black-framed mirror on the gallery mantelpiece is actually a black-bordered bereavement card.

I'd like to take a closer look but that would involve unhooking the black cord. Instead I decide to sketch the installation from where I stand. My notebook opens at an entry I made this morning. The second Edward Lipski text:

```
I got up at 8 and went
to the park and it was
bad and I saw a bird
and it was bad and I
went to the sea and it
was bad and I saw the
sun and it was bad and
I saw the moon and it
was bad.
```

I sketch the trolley. Trolley for whose last offices? Not Anthony – I can hear him on his word processor elsewhere in the building. Not me – I'm as well as can be expected in the circumstances. (What circumstances? Oh yes, I remember.) So it must be David McLaren. Dear dead David.

Cotton wool for his ears and nostrils. A cotton plug into his mouth and down his throat, the second pushed up his arse and the third... better shove that up his backside as well. All sealed up. Brush his hair just the way Davey liked it when he was alive and looking in a mirror... No, stop brushing his hair. Forget all that, in fact. A body is not required.

What now? Simply this. I slip the black cord from its hook

and pass into the room. I write 'David McLaren' on the bereavement card; then after a moment's thought add, 'Sadly passed away'; then after another pause add, 'And it was bad.' I move to the trolley and write 'David McLaren, RIP' on first one tag then the other but I don't go so far as to picture what parts of the body these will ultimately be attached to – there is really no need. And I place my clean and crisply folded copy of *Untitled* on top of the pile of towels.

Of course I do none of that. I don't want to upset Anthony, or his artist, and I'm looking forward to re-reading Bob Smith's diary. I'm looking forward to... Oh, all sorts of things.

I go outside.

Today   is   Tuesday

and   it   is

warm   and   sunny

John Stathatos
UNTITLED

Duncan McLaren
51 Sunderland Road
London SE23 2PS

Tel. 0181 291 6979

29 April, 1996

Dear John,

Thanks for the cheque for my contribution to UNTITLED 10 and the voucher copy. I like the way you've edited my Bob and Roberta review, but who is David McLaren?

I enclose a review of a project by Matthew Higgs that was showing at Anthony Wilkinson's until April 13. Can you use this?

Best wishes,

Duncan.

VENTRILOQUIST'S DUMMY

I wrote to Gilda Williams on 21 March enclosing a couple of texts. Now – 1 May – I can't wait to hear what she thinks about them. I must wait though, so I'm writing this.

I keep tripping over her name at the moment: she's written in *Art Monthly* for each of the last few months, and she's translated a review for the present issue of *frieze*. So, presumably, being an editor at Phaidon means swanning off to exhibitions at will (the in-tray can wait), researching and writing articles about the shows when back at the office (there's nothing important outstanding anyway), and brushing up on foreign languages the rest of the time (reading English can be *so* boring)... Hmmm. This paragraph was supposed to acknowledge that Gilda Williams is a busy professional, only it hasn't worked out that way. But let it stand.

I'd like to re-read her review of 'Young Americans' for the purposes of writing this, but it's Joanna who keeps the art mags so I won't get a chance until the weekend. However, I do have a copy of the current *Untitled* (it's great to see my name – well, a fair stab at it – in print), in which Gilda Williams is mentioned in connection with 'a new broom at Phaidon'. Apparently, the publisher... intends to make art more accessible... has attracted new writers from a variety of backgrounds... has headhunted emergent writers at the cutting edge, those 'who are articulating exciting views in a paradigmatic way'... I have a feeling that this article was written (commissioned and edited by John Stathatos) for the sole purpose of teasing my cock off.

The article tells me that the first five volumes of Phaidon's Contemporary Artists series are now published. Each includes interview, survey and focus sections. I'd fancy writing the focus bit on just about any artist you could mention (oh, stop it) but to test this out I should sample these five, surely. Jeff Wall is on the list and he's now showing at the Whitechapel, so yesterday I went there to buy the book. Unfortunately I got distracted by the large, back-lit transparencies mounted in light-boxes on display, especially by *A Ventriloquist at a Birthday Party in October 1947*.

Kids with balloons sitting in a living room, staring at the ventriloquist's dome-headed doll. There are a dozen of them on and around the sofa and armchair, the majority so transfixed that they've let go the ribbons of their balloons, which have floated up to rest against the ceiling.

In the video room downstairs, Jeff Wall explains that he set the scene in 1947 because that was when TV began to replace traditional entertainment. His interviewer then asks him if ventriloquism is also a metaphor for his own art or art in general. Wall admits he has given the doll certain qualities such as cunning, intelligence, wit – he's made it malicious, ancient, slightly dubious and not really suitable for children – which he thinks can be related to artistic qualities.

There were (say) a dozen of us sitting in three neat rows in the white cube, gazing at the TV screen. Most with notebooks open but pens not trying to keep up with the articulate stream of words coming from the sophisticated electronic head.

I'm not intending to write up Jeff Wall as a separate piece. Artist as centre-stage is a strong enough theme in my work already. Certainly in both the texts I've sent Gilda. I hope she doesn't think that this is my only theme (ah, but it is). I don't want her to think that at all. Other texts have different themes. 'Wing' is about humanity's relationship with animals; 'The Pledge of Fidelity' is about female attitudes influencing male attitudes; '15-Day Psycho' is about... What on earth is '15-Day Psycho' about?

Another question. Am I going to send this to Gilda Williams? Primarily, I'm writing it as a 'filler' for my book (what a lovely loose structure this book has; I hope I don't blow it). I'll decide if it would, on balance, be in my interests to send this as a 'letter' to Phaidon once it's finished. But I suspect I will send it in order to bring things to a head.

I hope Gilda phones me soon. I hope she doesn't phone before ten, since I'm a late riser and not very chatty first thing; I hope she doesn't phone when I'm watching the snooker, since the clink of ball on ball would be a dead giveaway that I don't have any job (ha!), never mind a high-profile one in art publishing; I hope she does phone, though, and that we have a constructive exchange of views.

There's a yellow balloon clinging to the ceiling of my room. The trick is to create static electricity by rubbing balloon against ventriloquist's dummy's hairpiece (or failing that something else nylon, like my green anorak). The balloon fell down for a while, but it was a piece of piss to get it up there again.

That's two genito-urinary references in three pages. I should censor at least one of them (How about 'inflating my hopes' instead of 'teasing my cock off'?) But I can't be fucked, I really can't.

Oh, good shot, Stephen!... That's two references to snooker inside a page, both of which should be jettisoned. But I can't see anyone beating him, I really can't...

•

Phoned Joanna this evening. Read aloud the letter in case she had any minor alteration to suggest. She told me that on no account should I send it: it wasn't appropriate for me to address

131

Ms Williams as Gilda, nor to refer to my cock or my anorak.

I'll take her advice and not post it. The ventriloquist's dummy – not so much cunning, intelligent and witty, but slightly desperate and not at all suitable for editors – is being put back in its strait-jacketed box. 'Gottle of geer!' it shouts, as the lid is closed.

I think I'll join you, mate.

8 May

Of course, shutting myself up in a box is not what I need right now. I need to get out of myself, my room; I need to get out and about. And I might as well combine this with researching another review for *Untitled*. This time it will not get too subjective. This time it will remain a disinterested, open-minded scrutiny of other people's work. Good...

Curators   Duncan McLaren
TRY
Royal College of Art

14 May, 1996

Dear Alex, Angela, Clare, Hannah and Rosie,

I thoroughly enjoyed visiting TRY. I hope you get something positive
from reading the enclosed review. I'd welcome your reactions to it.

Regards,

Gilda Williams   Duncan McLaren
Editor
Phaidon

14 May, 1996

Dear Gilda Williams,

I wonder if you've had a chance to look at the material I sent you in
March? If not, you won't thank me for sending you more to read, but I
enclose a review of the show 'TRY' on the grounds that it's short.

Regards,

John Stathatos   Duncan McLaren
UNTITLED

14 May, 1996

Dear John,

As I write, I don't know what you think of my Matthew Higgs piece, but
here is a review of an interesting show curated by MA students at the
Royal College.

Best wishes,

26 May

Phoned John Stathatos (not for the first time). He's been away for a couple of weeks but is about to start putting together the summer issue. However, he can tell me now that he can't use my review of 'TRY' since he'd commissioned someone else to review that show. He'll get back to me in a day or two about the Matthew Higgs piece... The call had begun with him apologizing for getting my name wrong in the current issue. But that is so much water under the bridge that it took me a second to realize what he was talking about.

There's no point in writing any more reviews as such. I do need to keep getting out and about, though...

PERSONAL DELIVERY

Pinned to walls of the Fruitmarket gallery in Edinburgh are life-size colour photos of alien-looking men standing in featureless white space. Each is wearing a crash helmet and brightly coloured synthetic overalls; each is holding out a red bag towards the viewer, but with varying degrees of conviction. Who are they? Where are they from? Where are the meetings taking place? What is being offered? What, if anything, is asked in return?

The handout tells me that over a period of time, artist Olivier Zabat ordered pizzas from home delivery services in Paris and then 'snapped' the pizza deliverers immediately they arrived. All my questions answered then; but I'm still curious. Again I walk around the gallery...

I stop in front of a dazzlingly blue-suited figure. He is standing square-on to me and seems to be holding back his bag rather than handing it over. His visor is down. It's tinted, so I can't see the features of his face never mind its expression. Intimidated, I move on...

That's better: visor up, I can see it's a human being I'm dealing with. He is facing me but slightly turned to the left, most of his weight on the back foot. He is presenting the bag towards me all right, its weight resting on the horizontal of his L-shaped right arm, while his left arm hangs limp by his side. His eyes are warily looking into mine; he is trying to keep a neutral expression on his face, but wariness – a combination of sensitivity and timidity – shines through. I reconsider the glossy red bag with its pair of metal-rimmed ventilation holes. Whatever it contains must be wide and stiff or the bag would flop down on either side of the supporting forearm; and it can't be heavy or he wouldn't be holding it out like that. A pizza would fit the bill, but somehow I can't believe it is a pizza, I look into his shy eyes again. The longer I stand here, the less comfortable he seems. I move on before he starts to tremble...

Different-coloured nylon suit, but this boy is remarkably similar to the last. From black helmet with fastened chinstrap down through right-angled arm to L-formation feet in off-white trainers, the posture is identical. One small discrepancy: this lad has the temerity to be clutching a chit in his left hand. I feel I could pull the piece of paper from his fingers and insert it in the identically held hand of the last delivery boy. But why would I want to do that? I wouldn't – his is not a well-paid job and to jeopardize the financial side of the transaction would be ridiculous behaviour. Money for pizza, that's the deal. So cancel 'temerity', he has every right to be clutching a bill in his hand. I stand there staring at it...

This one's from Pizza Hut, according to the badge-patch on his jacket. He's in basically the same pose as the last two. The limply hanging left arm is empty-handed but the L-shaped one supporting the bag is holding the chit between two fingers. This casual touch is undermined when I look down. His plastic trousers are much too long for him, bunching at the ankle and giving the impression that he is sinking to his knees. He needs to pull his trousers up. Either that or I need to pull them down by the ends, straightening the legs and covering up his untidy laces and grubby training shoes. However, I really must restrain myself. These hard-working lads have been placed in a vulnerable position, at the mercy of first their customer, who turns out to be an artist, and now the viewer, who turns out to be me. The artist has behaved himself; it's up to me to follow his example...

But, oh dear, look at the trainers on this guy! (And his red nylon trousers stop six inches short of the ground so it's difficult to look at anything else.) What has he been doing to them? Toe-piece holed, uppers stained and scuffed, laces untouchable, the gum-rubber band between uppers and soles hideous... It looks as if someone has taken a pizza topped with red peppers, mushrooms and green olives and smeared it over his feet. Perhaps as redress for wrong delivery ('I ordered red peppers, mushrooms and *black* olives, moron'). Perhaps as redress for late delivery: the whole work is called *30 Minutes*, so the possibility is that this pizza boy got held up, lost his way or crashed his L-plated scooter en route to the customer and was 'one minute late'! I tear my eyes away from his feet and take in the rest of him. As the others (helmet, bag, chit), but standing tall, shoulders back, with a warm, uncomplicated smile on his face. Which is excellent.

Another deliverer, but this one's been caught in the rain. Water shines white against the green of his nylon jacket. His clothes get wetter as they go down; I follow the course of several drops down the legs of his shiny trousers. Wettest of all are the folds bunched round his ankles. The green is darkest here and the reflections brightest. Below are pristine white trainers and these must be well soaked. Either the rain has washed them clean or this is a new pair. Sod's law says this is a brand-new pair gone soggy first time out. Smiling broadly, I look up to commiserate with the guy, but I'm jolted by his expression. Head back, eyebrows arched, nostrils flared, mouth pursed, he looks down his nose at me in deep disdain. Disgust even.

'It's all right, mate – I'm on your side,' I mutter.

His expression doesn't change.

•

Friday evening about eight. I skip down a flight of steps and firmly press the bell of the basement flat.

From the peep-hole in the door there must be a clear view of me in my helmet. Me in my helmet! I stand there, smiling keenly, looking forward to making my delivery.

'Who is it?' asks a cautious voice.

'Pret A Lire,' I say, self-confidence ringing in my ears.

'Visor up, please.'

'Oh, sorry.' I push the curve of transparent plastic up on to the dome of the helmet and smile into the peep-hole. I hear a snib being pushed and a handle turned. But the door opens a couple of inches only; it is on a chain. 'Who did you say you were?' asks a dark-haired, frowning woman.

'Pret A Lire,' I say, pointing to the PRET on my red helmet and the A LIRE on my green jacket. My other arm straightens – it thrusts forward in a decisive way – and presents her with the glossy red bag.

'What's that?' she asks.

'It contains a freshly made text.'

'I didn't order it.'

'That's not the way Pret A Lire operates.'

'I don't want it.'

'You think you don't want it. But actually...'

'Go away.'

'If you'll just...'

'Go away!'

'OK, OK. I'm going. But can I leave you with this chit?' And with my free hand I hold it out with some aplomb.

'If I don't want your product, I hardly expect the bill for it,' she says haughtily. 'Chit indeed!'

'It's not a run-of-the-mill delivery note-cum-invoice,' I tell her. 'It's simply an A4 sheet of paper with a few words typed on it.' And I unfold it twice, clear my throat and read in a clear voice: 'Dear Jo Bennett. Welcome to Pret A Lire – a radically fresh approach. In seven years Pret's passion and determination have taken me from a small single room in south London to that same small single room in south London.'

'I know where you live, Dunc,' she says dolefully.

'Thanks to the Italian Fast Food Association for voting me

Pizza Writer of the Year, 1996.'

'I've heard this before, Dunc,' she says. I try not to let her put me off.

'I continually strive for excellence and am never/always afraid to try something new. I never/always try to improve on nature by adding sugar, colourings, chemicals or preservatives.

'I have insisted my new text is made from paper derived from the Tampalla Foundation in Finland, where they currently plant ten thousand trees for every one they fell.

'My first "Helping the Homeless" scooter is not yet on the road. But soon many if not all of London's hostels for the homeless will be receiving my fresh texts free of charge.'

'Stop. All you've done is taken Pret A Manger's promotional blurb and substituted a word here and there. I wasn't impressed when you did it before and I'm not impressed now.'

I skip a couple of paragraphs and go on to the only new one, but I can't get rid of the sinking feeling in my stomach as I read: 'The courage of Pret A Lire activists is not legendary. Confronting modern whaling ships in a tiny inflatable armed only with a protest text? No, nothing like that.'

'Enough. All you've done is taken an extract from Friends of the Earth's literature and amended it slightly for your own selfish purpose. And in such a context that is pathetic... Absolutely pathetic.' She looks down her elegant nose at me in deep disapproval. Disgust almost.

Sighing, I turn away. I fold up my chit and make to shove it into a pocket. But my horrible clothes don't have any pockets so I have to hold on to it. It's raining. It's been drizzling since the afternoon. I was able to ignore that, but I can't ignore this downpour. I listen to the drops pounding my helmet and, bowing my head, consider my feet.

They've been cold for hours. Trainers always make my feet sweat. I think it's their synthetic lining, and that's what made them cold during earlier deliveries to a literary agent (no answer) and a Phaidon editor (the security guard wouldn't let me into the building). But now they're cold – blocks of ice – because of the rain. Water gets in through the eyelets, the ventilation holes (which I guess are there to stop my feet sweating) and, I'm fairly certain, through the stained and scuffed canvas of the uppers themselves. And once the water gets in it seems determined to stick around.

I walk away, footsteps squelching, a further squeaking noise coming from my right heel each time it makes contact with the ground. 'Wet far-*t*; wet far-*t*; wet far-*t*' is how my steps sound to my ears as I mount the stairs towards street level. Below me, I hear Joanna's voice through the pouring rain, asking, 'Is it true that the sexual prowess of Pret A Lire activists is legendary?'

I pause near the top of the steps. I am about to shake my head (she must be thinking of the lads from Pizza Fuck), but instead I have the presence of mind to nod and to say – albeit falteringly – 'Sure... sexual prowess... legendary.'

The door is thrown open and light pours out from within. I squelch towards that light. She asks only that I remove footwear and headgear before entering.

7 June

Phoned John Stathatos. He won't be publishing the Matthew Higgs piece (surprise, surprise). I ask why not. He tells me that it seemed to be following on from my review of Bob and Roberta, and he wasn't interested enough in that development. I admit that I thought he might respond in this way, which was why I'd sent him the more restrained review of 'TRY'. Had he read it? He'd only read it quickly (in view of the other commission), but what he'd like to do is to hang on to my two articles for a while, read them again at an early stage in the planning of the autumn issue and hopefully get back to me then. Nice of him to say this; but I'm not holding my breath...

Duncan McLaren
51 Sunderland Road
London SE23 2PS

10 June, 1996

Dear Mr McLaren,

On behalf of John Stathatos, Matthew Higgs, Gilda Williams, Bob Smith and
myself, I would like to thank you for your various communications of late
and for the ludicrous texts to which they refer. Please call it a day.

Yours sincerely,

Anthony Wilkinson.

The Bride of Jesus.

The Bride of Satan.

The Bride of Satan's doppelganger.

The Bride of Satan's doppelganger's hugger-mugger's literary executioner.

En Route

A wall-map of the streets of London is alongside a monitor playing a video of a man riding a scooter. The video has been taken from behind the windscreen of a car that's following the scooter over the humps and through the traffic lights of – I assume – London.

Sure enough, a route has been marked with red felt-tip on the wall-map. Start in Shakespeare Road, Camberwell, travel north to cross the Thames by Vauxhall Bridge, scoot along the embankment, recross the river by Westminster Bridge and return to the starting point through Lambeth and Brixton. Or have I got the journey the wrong way round?

The scooter parks outside a row of terraced houses and the rider dismounts and goes into a house... By the time the car has passed the bike and turned round, the rider has re-emerged from the front door. He kick-starts his vehicle and is off again down Shakespeare Road... At the T-junction he turns left. So it is, as I thought, a clockwise circuit – north then east, then south and west.

What is the point of the trip? Does he stop elsewhere on the route? I make myself comfortable – in the passenger seat of the following car as it were – and prepare to be patient...

Millbank. The Tate is on our left but the helmeted figure doesn't glance in its direction. We putter on... Parliament Square. Westminster Abbey to our left but the scooter rider is more concerned about the taxi behind him and to his right. He lets it pass before indicating and moving across. Now he is in the lane he wants for going over Westminster Bridge...

We don't stop at hospital or office or Imperial War Museum, and since we are now more than half-way through the circuit I don't suppose we will stop until we get to the house on Shakespeare Road. So what has the scooter rider been doing? Enjoying a breath of fresh air, the open road? Surely not. What, then?... I don't know.

Photos of road signs which have been altered. On the first, 'Strip Club' is in the same direction as Cambridge; straight on for the North, the West and Aylesbury. On the second, 'Slammer' is in the opposite direction to White City and Shepherd's Bush. The whole of the third is given over to an arrow and the words 'My House'. And on the fourth NO SMOKING is written on the carriageway itself where you might expect to read GET IN LANE.

I take in full details of one sign and walk over to the London street map. I see exactly where this sign must be. It's for traffic moving west along the Westway, and the prison in question is Wormwood Scrubs.

I reckon that another of the signs is in the vicinity of this show... Soon I am on the pavement of Great Eastern Street, standing between two thick metal poles and looking up at a substantial metal plate. On the back everything is painted the same matt grey. But the sign front is full of colour. It has a white border with rivet heads showing. The background is deep green except for patches of blue rimmed with white – for motorway references. Most of the letters and numerals are white but A-road codes are in yellow ochre.

Looking closely, I see that almost the whole surface is built up of small hexagons (the weave of the canvas, as it were), which must be something to do with light-reflective properties. But the words 'Strip Club', although otherwise consistent with the rest (style and size and spacing of letters), are not made of such material. They appear whiter, more insistent... I walk under the giant sign, do indeed turn right and am back again *En Route*.

Another map on the wall: an Ordnance Survey Pathfinder of the Isle of Sheppey. The island is at the mouth of the Thames estuary, in Kent, and its largest settlement is little Sheerness... It feels good to be taking a break from London.

The rack of postcards mounted beside the map emphasizes that the island is a low-key holiday resort. 'A POINT CHOSEN AT RANDOM' is marked on the map in a manner usually associated with 'YOU ARE HERE'. There are ten light bulbs protruding from the Pathfinder; underneath are switches next to labels naming places to visit in the area. There is nothing to compete with the major attractions of London, but then again perhaps that's exactly what 'pill boxes sprayed with Millwall graffiti', 'ponds of the mutant frogs', 'shrine of St Sexburga's pelvis' and 'site of Britain's first aircrash' do – they compete.

I flick the switch for 'nylon Y-front facility', but no bulb lights. I want to know where 'Europe's smallest nudist beach' is, but no glow. I flick each switch in turn (several times, even) but the lights are not connected, or are connected but don't work. However, my curiosity is aroused and I pore over the map, trying to locate for myself 'the cave of the Pram Man'.

There are bits and pieces resting on a table or stuck to the wall on either side of the map, so I browse through them. A cheap-day return from London to Sheerness dated 15 May 1996. A till receipt from Sheerness Co-op showing two bottles of Romanian wine, a pork belly slice, other items, all for less than ten quid. A doll with hair glued to its face called 'St Sexburga's Bearded Baby'. Apparently it forages for edible roots on wooded roundabouts, rummages through litter bins on petrol forecourts and (surprisingly for a creature with such a small inside-leg measurement) can run down second-hand camper vans and pizza delivery mopeds...

Turning back to the map, my eye goes straight to a circuit made up of B-roads in the middle of the island. And again I'm in the car, following the scooter that is trying to keep up with Bearded Baby as it makes its way clockwise from... let's say the first junction after crossing Kingsferry Bridge on to the island.

We approach a roundabout. A tourist information sign indicates left for 'original site of Halfway Housing Estate. Burned down in 1952 by Dutch sailors'; and right for Bearded Baby. The roundabout is unwooded, so right it is. Resuming cruising speed, Baby's legs are Road Runner blurred, which gives the impression he's on little wheels.

At the next junction BB slows to read the road sign, allowing the scooter to catch up, enabling the car to keep the whole thing on video. Left for 'the Monkey Farm'; straight on Bearded Baby...

The creature keeps to the NO SHAVING lane as it approaches Minster, and then unexpectedly stops on the main street beside a van parked on double yellow lines outside a bank. Baby extracts strips of white plastic from its nappied loins and places them on the ground at regular intervals and all around the vehicle, which has the phrase 'No job too large or too small' emblazoned across the side. Baby extracts more white plastic – letters now – and starts to lay them in a line on the road alongside the 'No job too...' flank of the blue van. I assume he's spelling out DOCTOR, but of course it's PLUMBER that's left in his wake.

The convoy stops again 100 yards further along the road, where a horrible caravan is ludicrously parked. Baby goes about his good deed again, this time using smaller letters, enabling him to spell out TRAINEE TATTOO OPERATIVE by the vehicle. I'm amazed, not only by Baby's powers of deduction, but also by the number of Ts he had (still has?) about his tiny person. By the time we leave Minster, parking spaces have also been reserved for CHECK-OUT GIRL (small Fiat outside chemist's), WAGES CLERK (Rolls outside bookie's) and another TRAINEE TATTOO OPERATIVE (spectacularly crap caravan, grotesquely inappropriate parking).

Where to from here? A postcard has been mounted face to the wall. The stamp is Dutch; the franking reveals the card came from Rotterdam. Its unseen picture is described as 'The Royal

Return, 15 May 1954. HMS *Britannic*, passing Greenwich'.

I wonder if this event is connected with the Dutch sailors running amok in Sheerness two years before. But I don't let this distract me from reading the postcard's neatly written message:

Dear All

Thank you for being here. It is nice of you to come. I hope that everything is going well and that you are in good health.

On the table please find some postcards, pens and pencils. I should be very grateful if you could maybe write to me and/or draw me a picture.

When you are done please leave the card on the table or hand it to the gallery staff.

They shall send me all the cards in one go when the show is over.

It will be very nice to receive all of the postcards on the same day.

Missing you,

Love, Jason

I read from the cards scattered haphazardly over the table: 'Not missing you', 'I hate you, Jason'. But many of the messages are friendly. I pick out a blank card from the pile of them and write, 'How do I carry on with this book I'm writing about contemporary visual art?'

Dropping the written card on to the table, I take another with me across the room to the Isle of Sheppey. The map tells me that there is a vehicle (V) and foot passenger (F) ferry ship service between Sheerness and Vlissingen and that the trip takes seven and a half hours by day, nine and a half hours by night. I take a note of this on the artist's card in case HMS *Britannic* is unavailable for his return.

The Isle of Sheppey is twinned with Rotterdam and there is, no doubt, a great metal sign on the island acknowledging the relationship – if only because it gives the council an excuse to show off its coat of arms: mutant frog, bearded baby, Pram Man and St Sexburga, each in a different-coloured pair of nylon Y-fronts, the whole copiously sprayed with Millwall graffiti. But I have a feeling that the twinning is not mutual, and that one could scour Rotterdam for a month without finding a sign that the city was twinned – or even had the most distant relationship (no, that's going too far) – with the humble Isle of Sheppey.

•

I travel to the wondrous Isle. Alas, the pressures of modern life go with me: I need money for ice-cream, petrol and chips; I need money for two bottles of Romanian wine, pork belly slice and pork belly whole; I need money for three pairs of Y-fronts (lavender, primrose and whatever the toilet word for blue is).

I pull up outside the bank on Minster High Street, place strips of white plastic around my vehicle (a second-hand fire truck) and neatly spell out the words WRITER AND ARTIST with white letters, which overlap annoyingly with the broken line down the middle of the road.

The cash machine asks for my unique PIN expression, so I tap in 'My Money'. Current balance £80. This is fine if my rent cheque has gone through but it means trouble (£0) if it hasn't. I really fancy an ice-cream-and-chip belly, though – to see if it lowers my self-esteem – so there was never any doubt about what I'd do next.

Suddenly flush, I turn round in time to see a traffic warden writing out a ticket for FRIAR TUCK. I point out the road markings protecting my vehicle. He looks up from his book and kicks out at a couple of letters, but discovers it's not so easy to move the plastic, which is vacuum-sealed to the tarmac. Nevertheless he slaps the ticket on the windscreen and tells me – tells the whole street – that reserved-occupation status is not for the likes of shite like me. 'Shite like me?' I say, intrigued by the concept. 'Shite like you, son,' he repeats, though I must be ten or fifteen years older than he.

I detach the ticket and read: 'Thank you for being here. It is nice of you to come. I hope that everything is going well and that you are in good health.'

I turn the page and my ticket gets even better:

James Young,
299b Shakespeare Road,
Camberwell,
London SE24 OQD.

(0171) 738 3055

DUNCAN,
          HERE ARE SOME ROAD SIGNS
AS REQUESTED. DO WITH THEM WHAT YOU
WILL.

JAMES

Duncan McLaren
51 Sunderland Road
Forest Hill
London SE23 2PS

Imagine you are navigating.

Imagine you are navigating.

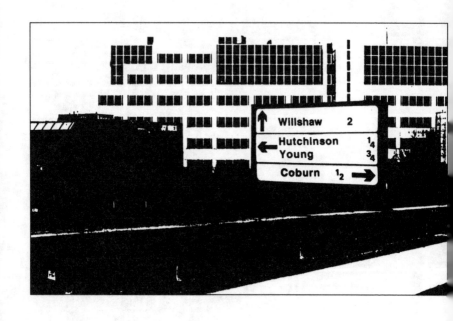

Q.   How do I carry on with this book I'm writing about contemporary visual art?

A.   (Tick box or boxes.)

☐   Depends what sort of book it is. But in any case...

☐   By going to exhibitions, engaging with the ideas and aesthetics of the
     artist, and responding imaginatively. (As perhaps you have been.)

☐   By asking editors, artists, bus drivers, friends, gallerists, literary
     agents, landscape gardeners and tattooists.

☐   Don't ask me.

☐   By listening to barking dogs, closing doors, passing cars and running water.

☐   By working out your motivation for producing this document.

☐   Don't give yourself a hard time - just go for it.

☐   Don't bother.

☐   "GO FOR IT, DUNC!"

☐   Nothing could persuade me to tick that last box.

☐   I'm tempted to tick the next box though.

☐   FUCK OFF.

☐   I shouldn't have done that - it seems a bit harsh. How would I like it if I
     sent out 200 copies of a carefully worded form and the only ones to come back
     told me to fuck off?

☐   Send me a list of artists whose work you've written about so far.

☐   Send me a sample text.

☐   I shouldn't have done that - what was I thinking of? Thank God I'd already
     taken the 'fuck off' option because it means I don't have to return this
     form. Only those who have ticked box 9 are legally obliged to return it.

☐   By engaging, entertaining and enchanting me - the wonderful reader.

☐   By flattering me (though 'wonderful' may be overdoing it) to return this form.

◯   That's enough boxes.

     (Or make another box and tick that.)

Dear Duncan McLaren

I have just received your questionaire which I have been expecting for some time now. Several of my friends have also received your multiple choice radtion and everyone who has always mentions it. This is, in a way, good news for you because it means people are paying attention. But, I have noticed some are dismisive about the questions you ask. Comments such as gratuitous, facetious + boyish have been passed when talking about your questionaire. I hope you are not upset by this, its just that I want to be honest + think you should have an insight into others reactions beyond ticks in boxes.

I am intrigued to see how your research manifests itself in written form, although I have already seen what you sent to Andrew Renton. I am intrigued as to why you chose En Route as a subject. Firstly because I never saw the show and secondly to see how you talk about the work (critically, anecdotally etc).

Anyway, whatever you do, be positive + enjoy it.

with regards

HOW IT FELT

To Tracey Emin's museum. A video is due to be shown at six p.m. The place is locked at quarter-to, so I step back to the edge of the road and take in the scene.

It's a converted shop flanked by a hairdresser's and a dentist's. Between white muslin drapes and the window THE TRACEY EMIN MUSEUM is spelt out on coloured cards. Sewn on to the muslin are letters:

THE

PERFECT

PLACE

TO GROW

Inside there are an array of watercolours on one wall, a projector pointing towards a screen close to the window front and a couple of benches.

I can't face it – there's only seating for half a dozen people and it may be that no one apart from me will turn up. So I'm walking towards Waterloo Station. I stop when I realize how I'd feel if no one turned up for a free film at my place. Back at the museum there are three people waiting outside. I stand staring into the dentist's surgery, as tense as if waiting for root-canal work.

Someone opens the door just after six, Tracey herself of course. One visitor sits on the blue bench, three on the pink, but there are paintings spread over half of the blue bench, so I park myself on the pink, close to the screen. After the artist/curator has listened to the messages on her answer machine and poured a plastic cup of water for those who want it, she walks up to me and asks if I'm sitting on something. 'Oh, sorry,' I say, standing up. Tracey picks up the piece of muslin, shakes it and hangs it over the door, on which she sticks a message. She tells us, 'If anyone comes to the window or the door while the film's on, just ignore them. They're too late... And I don't want any of you to leave while it's playing. Unless someone really has to.' Nobody speaks; there is nothing to say. Tracey adds that there is no smoking because she's got the only ashtray. She sits down on a home-made chair by the projector, dims the lights and rolls the film.

How It Feels was made in 1996 but refers to 1990. The film begins with Tracey sitting on the steps of a church, close to where her then doctor had a surgery. Prompted by questions from the cameraman, Tracey sets the scene.

She'd been told there was a 99.9 per cent probability that she could not become pregnant. But she had conceived. However, the doctor, some kind of Christian, wouldn't sign the papers required for a termination, and it was another five weeks before she obtained the necessary documentation. Tracey is angry at what the doctor did to her: his initial advice and the final insult.

Why didn't she have the child? Her life, at that time, was a mess, a failure, and if she couldn't look after herself how could she look after anyone else? She is angry and sad. Angry at the doctor and her old self; sad for her lost child.

In Regent's Park, Tracey talks about parenthood. She is cynical about people's motivation for having children – an ego- or a power-trip – and has no abstract wish to be a mother. But she admits specific regrets. The first of May is the anniversary of her abortion, putting a dampener on spring; September is when the child would have been born and the annual fall of leaves is especially poignant for her. She is scarred – her body, her eyes. She enjoys her life, which is full, but always there is something missing. The lost child.

In the vicinity of the clinic where it happened, Tracey recounts the story of her abortion. She and fifteen other women turned up as out-patients at nine a.m. She was asked if she wanted to go ahead with the termination. She (was it really her?) said yes, though the baby inside her was saying no. Tracey was last to be taken to the operating room in the afternoon. Before being sedated she was asked again if she wanted the termination. Tracey likes to think that as she lost consciousness she was trying to say no.

She awoke in what seemed like a morgue. She felt awful; she was discharged. At home she went to bed and stayed there. From day to day she felt worse. She managed to phone her doctor, who asked how she expected to feel after an abortion. After five days a friend came round, saw the state of her, contacted the hospital and was told to take her in straight away. As Tracey was getting out of the taxi – she was dressed as strangely as on the day of the operation, no knickers – she felt something slip out of her and down her leg. She held in her hands a second foetus.

The film ends on a more philosophical note, but the projector switching off and the lights going on still come too soon. There follows a contemplative – or is it an awkward? – silence... It's awkward now anyway, so I ask a question. Not the question I'd like to ask about double anniversaries and sorrows multiplied, but a straightforward one about human error.

Tracey answers. Then tells me that the film isn't so much about her abortion but failure in general. Perhaps it's only now that Tracey is successful as an artist that she's been able to confront earlier shortcomings. On the other hand, she feels that the film isn't entirely successful. She'd revisited the 1990 locations, expecting to feel liberated from and animated about her past experiences, but in fact she'd been morose and only spasmodically coherent. Most of the film shot had been unusable. The remainder was the best of a bad lot.

She tells us that the piece of art isn't finished yet. That it's still evolving as she plays the film to an audience twice each Thursday and Friday. Over the weeks it's become easier for her to watch the film, she's felt more comfortable with the question and answer session, and she's started to take an interest in abstract elements in the work – like when a taxi sounds its horn at a certain moment.

Another question from the audience. Nothing too probing, nothing confrontational, but Tracey's answer soon takes the conversation back into a challenging area – success and failure in art and life...

Seven o'clock. Others have turned up for the second performance. Tracey hands the visitors' book and a pen to the first of us. By the time the book gets to me everyone else has written a few words to thank Tracey, and signed their name. Artist Virgil Tracy was sitting (he's leaving now) at the other end of this bench. He persuaded Premier League football clubs to broadcast the message 'ONE VIRGIL TRACY, THERE'S ONLY ONE VIRGIL TRACY' on their electronic scoreboards during matches. But, judging by what he's written in this book, he – like the rest of us – has sat listening respectfully, apparently egoless, throughout the last hour.

So, what do I write? It's too late for spontaneity and too early, it seems, for something considered.

I sign the book. The signature is more or less legible. And I thank Tracey as I hand back her book and pen on the way out.

•

This is what I might have written in Tracey's book:

In the vicinity of the clinic where it happened, I recount the story of my abortion. Fifteen women and I turned up as outpatients at nine a.m. I was asked if I wanted to go ahead with the termination. I (was it really me?) said yes, though the baby inside me was saying no. I was last to be taken to the operating room in the afternoon. Before being sedated I was asked again if I wanted the termination. I like to think that as I lost consciousness I was trying to say no.

I awoke in what seemed like a morgue. I felt awful; I was discharged. At home I went to bed and stayed there. From day to day I felt worse. I managed to phone the doctor, who asked how I expected to feel after an abortion. After five days a friend came round, saw the state of me, contacted the hospital and was told to take me in straight away. As I got out of the taxi – I was dressed as strangely as on the day of the operation, no knickers – I felt something slip out of me and down my leg. I held in my hands a second foetus.

Or, more simply, this:

I (was it really me?) said yes, though the Baby inside me was saying no.

Q. <u>How do I carry on with this book I'm writing about contemporary visual art?</u>

A. (Tick box or boxes.)

☐ Depends what sort of book it is. But in any case...

☑ By going to exhibitions, engaging with the ideas and aesthetics of the artist, and responding imaginatively. (~~As maybe... you have been.~~) *Probly NOT BEEN*

☐ By asking editors, artists, bus drivers, friends, gallerists, literary agents, landscape gardeners and tattooists.

☐ Don't ask me.

☐ By listening to barking dogs, closing doors, passing cars and running water.

☑ By working out your motivation for producing this document.

☐ Don't give yourself a hard time - just go for it.

☐ Don't bother.

☐ "GO FOR IT, DUNC!"

☐ Nothing could persuade me to tick that last box.

☑ I'm tempted to tick the next box though.

☐ FUCK OFF.

☐ I shouldn't have done that - it seems a bit harsh. How would I like it if I sent out 200 copies of a carefully worded form and the only ones to come back told me to fuck off?

☑ Send me a list of artists whose work you've written about so far.

☐ Send me a sample text.

☐ I shouldn't have done that - what was I thinking of? Thank God I'd already taken the 'fuck off' option because it means I don't have to return this form. Only those who have ticked box 9 are legally obliged to return it.

☐ By engaging, entertaining and enchanting <u>me</u> - the wonderful reader.

☐ By flattering me (though 'wonderful' may be overdoing it) to return this form.

◯ That's enough boxes.

(Or make another box and tick that.)

☑ I dont understand why you have sent out This form are you craving for attention That Emilia

STRANGE CHILD

To the Centre for Contemporary Arts on Glasgow's Sauchiehall Street, where David Shrigley is showing new sculpture.

The wall-mounted list of works indicates that the pile of pink tubing in a corner of the gallery is *A Strange Toy for a Strange Child*. I walk towards it.

Head and tail emerge from tube tangle. A snake's head, although the eyes, nose and mouth cursorily drawn on its top surface might be human. But a snake's head because it's on the end of what is undoubtedly a snake's body. Eighty metres of it, according to the CCA handout.

The pink skin is mottled. I bend to stroke it: simultaneously smooth and rough. Satin accounts for the smooth, but whence the rough? Squeezing the neck, beads of polystyrene come to mind.

My eyes follow the neck into the confusion of loops and coils. To follow further I walk clockwise around the pile... I need to thrust a hand into the tangle to see where the body goes from here – it loops back on itself... I get so far, then I have to give up when the next confusion – not a knot, the tubing is never constricted – occurs too near the centre of the nest of snake for me to mentally untangle it without wading in there. It's not my place to wade in there and straighten things out. I back off.

A sheet of white paper lies on the floor. A fibreglass cast of a sheet of paper, rather. The cast replicates the crinkles and creases of the original sheet, which was folded in four at one time. What size is it? A1, perhaps. But, no, each of the quarters is bigger than A4, though not, I think, as large as A3. I'm not in my usual relation to paper – I'd need a table and chair for that – so it's difficult to be sure.

From white rectangle to roughly circular black patch, *Crud*. Latex simulates a patch of tar that has melted and then been prodded and poked and stood on, the footprints and other marks preserved in the tar, now reset. Two white eyes with black pupils have been painted on the patch, giving the impression of a face. Stoic or embittered or what? I wouldn't like to say. Not yet, anyway.

Rising up from the floor is a lamppost, a scale-model streetlight. Grey-painted metal; a wider tube at the bottom, it narrows and remains so to the top and along the overhang. The glass-encased light is on. I stand directly under it, my hair grazing the glass, a Colossus, though the title of the piece, *Lanky Git*, lays a different emphasis. I survey the scene: snake, paper, crud. 'Unrealized potential' and 'lowest of the low' are phrases that seem to apply here. But I haven't seen the fifth and last exhibit yet.

A red-backed book has been mounted face to the wall. Author's name and book's title appear on the spine – *The Bloodied Spear* by Nid E. Spranbranker. The back cover tells me that the book has been translated (with an introduction and notes) by Lucky Bruce Thompson.

Then come quotes: 'A detective novel, a religious epic, a study in criminal psychopathy'. 'The most confusing novel I have read since the war.'

Next comes blurb: 'Imagine you are God. You are omnipotent and have power to punish wrongdoers in fantastic biblical ways. Remember that terribly mean thing you said to me yesterday? How would you punish such wickedness as that? Lightning? Plague? Pestilence? – In your case the punishment is no fags. I have smoked all your fags myself, thus making me an instrument of God's will.'

The use of the second person here is confusing. 'You... have power to punish wrongdoers' alongside 'In your case the punishment is no fags' suggests that punisher and punished are one and the same.

Apparently the front cover shows a child falling into a canal, but I can't see this for myself because the book is held face hard against the wall by two clasps top and bottom. But the set-up hasn't stopped visitors from investigating whether or not the pages of the book are actually printed, judging by faint smudges across the page ends. I let my own fingers follow the line of least resistance and prise pages apart just enough to see that they are (of course) blank.

I stand under the streetlight again, resurveying the scene.

•

I'm lying on the floor in the middle of my brother's flat that's so handy for the CCA. Feeling a bit low. Why?

I want tea but there's no milk; there's no coffee either. But it's not that. John said I could use his flat today as long as I left a tidy kitchen behind me. When I agreed to this I had no idea of the room's present state: binbag overflowing, sink and washboard dish-full, cooker filthy and disturbing.

On one of the rings is a frying pan containing dark-green-cum-black stuff. Vegetable curry, as was. It's partially desiccated – the surface is cracked – but it's still moist underneath. I poked a bit that obtruded, and off slipped dark skin to reveal a white oval patch of potato. I uncovered a second potato piece, so that the pan's resemblance to *Crud* became unmistakable.

I felt slightly better when I entered the lounge, because of an immediate discovery. There was a broadsheet newspaper lying folded on the floor. Discarding all but the outside page, I unfolded it to reveal a sheet the same size as the one in the gallery and with required creases. I folded it back together, crumpled it slightly with a blow from my fist, then spread it out over the floor. Perfect. Except for all the words of course.

Then I felt low again when I realized there was nowhere to sit. Well, there's a bean-bag, and a futon pushed into the shape of a settee, but I wanted something on legs and there is nothing on legs. This goes for John's TV, sound system, typewriter and bed – none of them is raised above the floor. How does he eat meals? Write letters? Can he do it all from a prone position?

I hear a rumble from down below. It might be my stomach – it's lunchtime after all. It might be my large intestine (now, why would I think that?). But I know it's the sound – with accompanying vibration – of an underground train. The sound loudens, then fades away... I can't tell if it passed parallel to my bodyline or perpendicular to it. Maybe next time. But is such rumbling, such shallow tunnelling, really necessary? The situation in London would seem to be preferable, where they have tubes all right, hundreds of them, but they move in deep-enough tunnels not to bother the surface dwellers.

Back to me feeling down. I felt low even before I arrived at the flat. I felt low as soon as I saw the lampposts at this end of Sauchiehall Street. The same grey colour and elegant shape as David Shrigley's but hugely different. Standing under one, I looked up and a few feet above head height a notice said, 'No stopping except local buses'. I felt uncomfortable but I stood my ground and raised my eyes. Yards above head height was a mounted poster on behalf of Scottish Labour, presumably left over from an election. I felt more comfortable, so I stayed where I was and raised my sight to the top of the lamppost. It was miles away!' Making me feel such a short-arse. Shortest of short-arses. Lowest of the low.

Tube alert. My ear and cheekbone are to the floor. The insides of my forearms down to the palms of my hands are resting on carpet also, sensitive to the vibration. My stomach, thighs, knees and toes are all making a contribution: gripping, pressing, tapping or whatever it takes to get me in touch with what's going on under the surface... The tube comes from beyond my head (west), passes along the length of my body but some distance to the right – say, under Kent Road itself – and slips beyond my feet (east). So now I can relax about that and concentrate on the other.

The low feeling originated pre-Glasgow. From something John said when we were talking politics. He claimed my views on education were a joke, the result of leading an atypical, isolated existence, and that they would remain a joke until I got out and about and met a few real people living real lives.

What a terribly mean thing to say. John must be punished for attacking me in this way. Unfortunately, thinking of punishments for loved ones is not my strong suit. Clearly I'm not going to stretch a leg in order to switch off his amplifier, or slide my arm into the bathroom so as to flush the toilet, or lift my little finger for him in the kitchen. But that's not punishment enough.

I'm quite happy to lie here. Without moving an inch. Until a suitably fantastic punishment – biblical or otherwise – comes to mind.

•

Earlier this year I saw an exhibition of David Shrigley photos at the Photographers' Gallery in London. A show I recommended to John, partly because I felt that some of the pictures had been taken near to his flat.

Here, for example. On the pavement, close to the kerb, a pole sticks up from the ground at an eighty-degree angle, its parking restriction sign missing. As in Shrigley's photo there are bin-liners of refuse placed around the foot of the pole, though the sculpted head placed on top – presumably by the artist – is no longer there. I walk on.

Or maybe this is the site. Leaning pole; missing sign; bags of rubbish. Frankly I think Glasgow council has backed a loser here. Obviously drivers don't see the poles when parking. Just as obviously pedestrians do see them, some rising to the challenge of removing the sign, others paying obscure homage to the poles by surrounding them with garbage. Anyway, without the photo to refer to I can't be sure which of these Kelvingrove streets it was taken in.

However, the CCA's handout for what's on this month advertises the Shrigley show with a reproduction of another photo, *Lost*. I take it out and scrutinize:

If the photo was taken here in Kelvingrove Park I should be able to locate the exact spot.

The park is bounded on two sides by a three-storey Victorian terrace. Glimpses of a pillared porch and three floors of white-silled windows in the background of *Lost* suggest I am indeed in the right place. One terrace is on top of a steep rise, so I can discount that. The other is behind railings, which I can't make out in the fuzzy background but which might well be there.

I walk towards a tree. No good – the trunk is vertically marked rather than horizontally... These trees are all lime trees, their barks similarly marked... This ash tree is more like it, but there are no trees between it and the houses. I move on, on the lookout for a unique juxtaposition of ash tree, parkland and Victorian terrace...

'Specky twat.' This comes from the direction of a couple of youths. There is no one apart from me close to them, never mind anyone else wearing specs. The words spoken may have something to do with the football that bobbled in front of me and which I ignored. Of course! They wanted me to abandon my own agenda long enough to return the ball to them. Now, there is a way to handle this situation and a way not to handle it. But it is course B that will bring me in contact with real people leading real lives, so here goes.

I show them the postcard. Predictably enough, they think I am looking for a bird. I explain that I am a culture vulture rather than a pigeon fancier and they seem to take this in. Certainly I have their attention. 'Severe haircut,' I say, pointing to the head of one. 'Incipient beer belly,' I say, pointing to the stomach of the youth wearing a Rangers top. To rob this last remark of any possible offence, I point to my own midriff and repeat it. Self-deprecation always goes down well with people who have such an inherently defensive attitude. Though, ironically, the defensive attitude so often manifests itself in displays of aggression.

One makes a disparaging observation (about me) to his mate. I ask if they could switch from local dialect to 'RP'. Not because I can't understand them, but so that I don't seem patronizing when I come to write this up. They stand and stare. 'Received pronunciation,' I say, helpfully.

'This English cunt is taking the piss,' is said, word perfect. However, I feel the need to point out that I am a London-based Scot, just as David Shrigley is a Glasgow-based Englishman (as far as I know). Of course, being London- or Glasgow-based implies nothing about where one might be at any particular time. Just as I am here in Glasgow now, David must have visited London this year for his shows at the Photographers' Gallery and at Stephen Friedman's.

I must tell the pair about an exhibit in the Friedman show.

Lying on the gallery floor was a single, much larger than life, green leaf. It was made of rubber, cast from a lime tree leaf, possibly/quite probably/almost certainly a lime tree leaf plucked from this very park. Such a fresh green it was; such a heart shape it had; such a serrated edge there was to it. It really made me feel that spring was just round the corner. It really made me think of Glasgow – this dear, green place.

Meanwhile, I've been frogmarched to the middle of a bridge. No grass, no trees, no housing. 'This isn't the place,' I scoff. Suddenly I am swung off my feet and am staring down into a shallow can-strewn river, thirty feet below. I see their point: the river now dominates my field of vision in exactly the way the tree trunk does in the photo. An interesting metaphor, but somewhat by the way.

Realizing that I'm being held against my will in a precarious position above the river, I decide to talk my way out of it. 'Imagine you are God. You are omnipotent and have power to punish wrongdoers in fantastic biblical ways. Remember that terribly wicked thing you said to me earlier? How would you punish such wickedness as that? Lightning? Plague? Pestilence? – In your case the punishment is no beer. I have drunk all your cans of McEwan's lager myself, thus making me an instrument of Strathclyde police's will.'

'Shut it, creep.' And despite my wriggling and writhing the centre of gravity of my body is now definitely the wrong side of the parapet. Luckily I remember a trick Brer Rabbit played on Brer Fox, one easily adapted to my present circumstances. 'I don't care what you do to me, lads,' I say, 'so long as you don't fling me in that river. Tar me, feather me, tar-and-feather me, lads, but *don't* fling me in that river!' (Have I got this right? It was definitely a Nid E. Blyton book, Lucky Brer Rabbit was certainly involved, but was the little devil bluffing or double-bluffing? Oh well, I dare say I'll find out.)

'Cheers, mate.'

They drop me; I'm falling; John will be sorry now. What a strange sen

Q. How do I carry on with this book I'm writing about contemporary visual art?

A. (Tick box or boxes.)

☐ Depends what sort of book it is. But in any case...

☐ By going to exhibitions, engaging with the ideas and aesthetics of the artist, and responding imaginatively. (As perhaps you have been.)

☐ By asking editors, artists, bus drivers, friends, gallerists, literary agents, landscape gardeners and tattooists.

☐ Don't ask me.

☐ By listening to barking dogs, closing doors, passing cars and running water.

☐ By working out your motivation for producing this document.

☑ Don't give yourself a hard time - just go for it.

☐ Don't bother.

☐ "GO FOR IT, DUNC!"

☐ Nothing could persuade me to tick that last box.

☐ I'm tempted to tick the next box though.

☐ FUCK OFF.

☐ I shouldn't have done that - it seems a bit harsh. How would I like it if I sent out 200 copies of a carefully worded form and the only ones to come back told me to fuck off?

☐ Send me a list of artists whose work you've written about so far.

☐ Send me a sample text.

☐ I shouldn't have done that - what was I thinking of? Thank God I'd already taken the 'fuck off' option because it means I don't have to return this form. Only those who have ticked box 9 are legally obliged to return it.

☐ By engaging, entertaining and enchanting me - the wonderful reader.

☐ By flattering me (though 'wonderful' may be overdoing it) to return this form.

○ That's enough boxes.

(Or make another box and tick that.)

JOHN WEARING
RANGERS F.C.
BOBBLE HAT

GREY + WHITE
PIDGEON

IN CASE
JOHN FALLS
IN RIVER

CLYDE

1966 A.D.

174

REAL LIFE vs. NATURE

I'm in a farmhouse in Aberdeenshire. Greenwards By Hatton, Peterhead, to be specific. Lured here – it's a two-hour drive from my parents' place – by a paragraph and a photo in *The List*. 'What's On in Glasgow and Edinburgh', indeed.

But the room I'm standing in is a white cube all right, and the single piece of work installed is of the sort that I'd only associate with an urban contemporary art space. A wooden shed that's too small to enter, raised on legs, with four pencil-shaped wooden posts penetrating and protruding from its sides; a cassette player held aloft – by rope tied to the pencil posts – playing traditional Scottish music backwards; the words 'I' and 'MESSIAH AM JAILER' marked on adjacent gallery walls.

On the room's window ledge is documentation relating to the gallery. A copy of *Flash Art* reviews an earlier show here at Iain Irving Projects. The review is written by Judith Finlay, Iain's partner in this remote rural spot, but there is no mention of these facts in the review. 'By all accounts there are some interesting things happening in...err... Greenwards By Hatton,' says a reader in Milan or Paris or Berlin. Diaries are extracted, windows found and an intention pencilled in. In one sense the review is a joke that only a few art insiders will appreciate. Quite funny, though.

Iain enters and we chat. He is open and friendly, as I'd expected – it was his telephone manner that finally persuaded me to make this morning's long drive. In his view, the journey to the space is an important element of the experience here. And his next show would seem to acknowledge this: 'A Fast Moving Car' relates to that moment, particularly when driving, when you are looking at something but are thinking about something completely different, says a leaflet handed to me.

The card for Dalziel and Scullion's recent show here is on the window ledge. A photo taken from the driving seat of a car; a deer in the middle of the road, mesmerized by the headlights. Iain tells me that in setting up the picture, Louise and Matthew were stopped by a policeman who assumed they were poaching. It was pointed out that the deer was stuffed and that they were taking photographs for their work. But the policeman couldn't reconcile his notions of art practice to what was happening and went ahead with the arrest.

The card for the present show is also on display. Ross Sinclair,

trousers rolled up to the knees, standing in the shallows looking out to sea. He isn't wearing a shirt so the REAL LIFE tattoo across the top of his back is to the fore. The artist faces a lighthouse. Peterhead? I ask Iain. But the photo was taken a few miles further along the coast, at Rattray Head. If I'd come all the way from Milan or Prague or Berlin I might travel this extra distance – it would be interesting to see the full context in which this photo was taken. But as it is I won't be driving any further.

Anyway, there's more to see here. And when Iain hands me a mug of coffee, I take it with me into the hedged garden.

Another Ross Sinclair hut on stilts. But this one is bigger, higher, and there's a ladder leading up inside it. I step up and am soon sitting comfortably, back resting against a wooden panel, feet and elbows on handy ledges. The view is wide open to me, divided – by wooden poles supporting the pitched roof – into left, right and straight ahead sections.

Wide blue sky with rolling clouds over wide, rolling farmland. A few fields of green pasture, but mostly the land is arable. The large field straight ahead has been harvested recently and is studded with great rolls of straw. One large field to the right and in the distance has been ploughed again already; another far away to the left hasn't been harvested yet, its light-brown crop rippling in the breeze that I'm protected from by the wooden backboard, a breeze from the west.

It's great here, I love it. There's plenty to stimulate me without recourse to the nearly full bottle of whisky that's balanced on a shelf under the eaves. Someone (the artist?) has written 'drink me' on the label, so I reach out for the bottle, unscrew the top and sniff the contents. The real thing. But I've got a coffee and a car and this view for Christ's sake, so I return the bottle untasted.

Hard down to my right is the farm proper, run by a farmer Iain was telling me about. He's friendly enough, but is at a loss to understand why people travel all this way for a transaction that doesn't seem to involve money changing hands. He is there now, standing in the farmyard beside a grain tower which is making a noise. Is he drying oats? I don't know. He's staring right at me.

I ignore him. That's to say I look to my left for a solid minute.

But when I glance down to the right again he's still there, looking this way. Perhaps he thinks I'm a poacher or, more likely, a rustler: spying out the land in preparation for a night sortie; working out how to get three rolls of straw, two cows and a horse into my aunt's Fiesta. Perhaps he wants me to tell him where his combine harvester is. That hulking great red thing? It's by the gate in that newly done field, mate. Where you fucking well left it...

But I must cast off my brutish urban instincts. This is a tranquil place and Iain's told me the farmer is all right. He puts root vegetables in the middle of the rolls of straw (how does he do that?). These are cooked over the winter by the release of heat from the stalks of oats, so that when the animals get into the centre of their winter feeding they get a bonus, a special treat, a taste sensation.

In the narrow grass field directly in front of me, two cows and a horse are feeding on a relatively new roll of straw. All three are munching away to the one apparent end, but for all I know are at cross-purposes – the cows hoping for roast parsnips, the horse looking forward to potatoes baked in their jackets.

I lean back and rest my shoulder blades against the wooden backrest. REAL LIFE, certainly. But it doesn't have to be real life versus nature. I must cast off my cynical urban perspective and open myself to the reality all around me.

In the distance, in the centre of my view, is the main road running north – south. Vehicles move from right to left (the way I came) before disappearing behind a roll of hill. Vehicles move from left to right (my way home) before disappearing likewise.

My way home. I suppose I'd better be going. No, not yet – I'm still hoping to melt into the view...

This road is terrible. It's a dual carriageway and you have to change lanes all the time: overtaking the slow vehicles and then getting back into the inside lane to allow faster cars past. Part of the problem is that I don't drive often enough and have never really had experience of this or motorway driving. I don't know exactly how to interpret what's in my rear-view mirror, and my use of the wing mirror just isn't good enough – I reckon there's a blind spot at least the length of a car. I'm learning to lean forward when I use the wing mirror, but am not yet doing this consistently. I'm tense the whole time.

Of course, some people have to use this road every day. And no doubt they become proficient drivers. But there are still situations likely to arise where no amount of sound judgement helps. I keep thinking about them. There is no way I'm going to relax until I'm off this bloody road.

I need to get past that lorry. Foot down; stare into the middle distance; ignore the massive wheels and the mid-carriageway kerb equally. Oh, God, we're going downhill now, the lorry's speeding up and the road is bending to the left. I need to keep my foot down, and turn the wheel towards the lorry – not that much – and keep looking into the middle distance.

FUCK! What is that tractor doing? Oh, don't come out, for God's sake. But I'm past it now (what a fucking road this is, with traffic coming on and going off via the outside lane), so I stare into the middle distance, and steer slightly away from the lorry, and keep my foot down.

There. Overtaking manoeuvre complete; life status, normal. I glide back into the inside lane but keep my speed up because there is a clear road in front. I stretch out my arms and straighten my back, feeling my shoulders pressing into the supportive seat. My back feels sticky with sweat. STILL ALIVE, though.

Wide blue sky with rolling clouds over wide, rolling farmland. A few fields of green pasture, but mostly the land is arable. The large field straight ahead has been harvested recently and is studded with great rolls of straw. One large field to the right and in the distance has been ploughed again already; another far away to the left hasn't been harvested yet, its light-brown crop rippling in the breeze that I'm protected from, a breeze from the west.

It's great here, I love it. In the distance, in the centre of my view, is the main road running north – south. Vehicles move from right to left (the way I came) before disappearing behind a roll of hill. Vehicles move from left to right (my way home) before disappearing likewise...

Hang on a minute, that road rings a bell.

Oh, yeah – right.

EDINBURGH MAN

I'm about to leave Stills Gallery in Edinburgh. 'Tales from the city' is the theme of the show; five well-known artists; but somehow... It's probably my fault. I met my brother and, for the first time, his girlfriend, Lucy, at lunch today. And that's taken the edge off my energy. I should have taken a break before coming here. Oh, well.

Before going I look out of a side window. I have to look again. God, that's amazing. I'm blinking away and having to make an effort not to make noises of appreciation: coos, whoops, gurgles, diabolical laughter. I'm smiling hugely.

Down there is a pend, a small close surrounded by the backs of four- and five-storey stone buildings. I look them up and down. Grey, Edinburgh stone *en masse*. The sombre walls are punctuated at regular intervals by narrow windows, all of which must have essentially the same view down on to the back area as I do. I'm smiling again.

Nearly filling the close is a burial mound the length of an adult human. A cross sticks up from the heaped earth at one end. Is it for real? (Is it for real!) Is it part of this show? If it is part of the show, then how come the local residents put up with such a monstrous object (glorious thing) under their daily noses?... I'm not sure I want answers to these questions. But I know I'm too curious to play that game.

I ask at the desk. It's a piece by David Shrigley. The pend is owned by the city council and is in use only as a fire exit for the surrounding buildings. No comment has been forthcoming – adverse or otherwise – from a single local resident.

•

I was distinctly dubious about this pub from the outside, but the place on the opposite side of Leith Walk looked like a deathtrap.

I was still dubious when I approached the bar, conscious of the energetic discussions going on around it. But there was a reassuring air about the publican – trousers sharply creased, hair crisply side-parted, a respectable, old-fashioned type; the sort who'd run a tight ship – so I bought a pint.

Good decision. Away from the bar the place is empty. There is a lone table in an alcove lit by a spherical lamp, the walls covered with orange textured wallpaper: The Temple of the Golden Pavilion. I sit at it. Of course I fucking do. Splendid isolation.

I always have a pint when I'm out and about in Edinburgh. Whereas in London I never do. There's something about the atmosphere in this city that encourages brooding introspection. The steep cobbled streets, the high stone-walled buildings, the ever-present castle, the dark pubs. The scattered inhabitants nursing pints and bolting chasers. Jekyll and Hyde territory.

I open *Untitled*, which I shouldn't have bought at the gallery – it's London-orientated and will distract me from the here and now, but it's too late. Page three: a full-page photo taken by John Stathatos of Bob Smith standing outside the Saatchi Gallery. Bob looks glum. The gate is closed and spikes on top make it unclimbable. Bob holds a placard. On a square of cardboard fixed to a wooden pole have been stuck letters forming the message:

AT FIRST
THE
SARCHY   BROTHERS
WROTE   SONGS.
PENNY   LANE
WAS   ONE
OF   THEIRS

Familiar stuff. Right now Bob Smith has the Chisenhale gallery full of his texts featuring art-world people, pop icons and misspellings. One huge text dominating the gallery tells of how Yoko Ono gave 'She Loves You' to her lover Joseph Beuys, only for the two to split and for Beuys to send the record to her new lover, John Lennon, with a note saying 'and you can have her, mate'.

Doubly familiar. I saw another text piece on cardboard recently, by someone else. It simply said 'Saatchi' along the top, 'SAATCHI' along the bottom, with the words "'n' motherfuckin" painted in between. I liked that. But can I like this so soon after liking that?

It's too similar to what Bob's been doing. Too similar to what other artists are doing. (They're all at it just now – Saatchi this and Saatchi the other. Change the record, lads, please.) OK, so Bob would like to fill Saatchi's wonderful gallery, and feels the time is right now that he's exhibited this year at a West End commercial gallery and at an East End public space. But this can't be the way to go about it – the same route everyone else is taking.

My pint has gone; it slipped down nicely. Things seem to be heating up at the bar – there's a lot of effing and blinding going on about the quality of joinery these days. Can't get a decent coffin for love nor money?... I'd better be going.

•

I'm in John's car. He's driving us north towards our parents' house. It's dark, it's raining, the road is busy and we're going too fast. But I don't say anything. Or, rather, I talk about Lucy, her job, John and his job.

The road is a little clearer now, the rain easing. I've been wanting to know what John thought of my David Shrigley text for a while now and this is my chance to find out. Of course he won't be able to remember, so I introduce the subject by saying that Dad's just read it. Dad just about coped with the scene in the gallery and the scene in John's flat, but completely lost the plot in part three, when the action takes place in the park. John tells me that this was more or less his own reaction. The bit with the pigeon-postcard in the park was all right, but the scene with the two youths didn't work for him – there didn't seem to be a connection with the sculptures that were the starting point of the chapter.

I tell John that there was a connection with two of the sculptures – the cruddy tar face and *The Bloodied Spear* wall-mounted book. (Was there another specific connection? I can't think of one offhand.) But my main justification for it was that all David Shrigley's work was steeped in a Glasgow ambience and I wanted my text on his work to be that way also.

John feels I went too far (my scene was too hackneyed) or not far enough (my incident could have been longer, with real people and street dialogue).

I try again to justify my writing, but find myself repeating points and, finally, blustering. John shrugs and tells me that all he's doing is stating a point of view. But adds that it's curious that his own viewpoint coincides with Dad's.

I'm silent. I'm silent because we're going so fast into driving rain and I want to get home in one piece.

Change of subject (but still art, of course). I tell John about Bob Smith's project for *Untitled*. I'd show him the page itself but I don't want John to take his eyes off the road for one second. But I describe the photo and he gets the picture. I start to slag it off, only to find John defending it. The Saatchi ad that everyone remembers is the one they did for the Tories – 'Labour Isn't Working'. And the image that goes with 'Labour Isn't Working' is a queue of the unemployed outside a Job Centre (Penny Lane, indeed). Bob's photo conjures up a great line of underemployed artists outside the Saatchi Gallery. But then brings you back to just Bob on his tod. In John's opinion this is art rich in ambiguity: Bob Smith connecting with a downtrodden and deceived working class; Bob Smith recognizing himself as just another artist aspiring to pop-star fame. Ironic and self-aware work.

I'm silent. I'm silent because of our speed, and the rain, and the truck that we're overtaking on this bend, for Christ's sake. The windscreen wipers can't cope and I'm expecting a sidewind to hit us any moment now.

I look straight ahead, peering into the night. I see earth heaped into a burial mound. There's a stone at one end, I can't help noticing. And when I look closely I can read words:

R.I.P.

DUNCAN MCLAREN

NEVER REALLY GOT ON TOP OF THINGS.

ON THE DAY HE DIED, HIS BROTHER –

AFTER A HARD DAY'S WORK, AND WHILE

DRIVING IN ATROCIOUS CONDITIONS –

RAN RINGS ROUND HIM ON HIS OWN

SPECIALIST SUBJECT.

Q. How do I carry on with this book I'm writing about contemporary visual art?

A. (Tick box or boxes.)

☐ Depends what sort of book it is. But in any case...

☐ By going to exhibitions, engaging with the ideas and aesthetics of the artist, and responding imaginatively. (As perhaps you have been.)

☐ By asking editors, artists, bus drivers, friends, gallerists, literary agents, landscape gardeners and tattooists.

☐ Don't ask me.

☐ By listening to barking dogs, closing doors, passing cars and running water.

☐ By working out your motivation for producing this document.

☐ Don't give yourself a hard time - just go for it.

☐ Don't bother.

☑ "GO FOR IT, DUNC!"

☑ Nothing could persuade me to tick that last box.

☐ I'm tempted to tick the next box though.

☐ FUCK OFF.

☐ I shouldn't have done that - it seems a bit harsh. How would I like it if I sent out 200 copies of a carefully worded form and the only ones to come back told me to fuck off?

☐ Send me a list of artists whose work you've written about so far.

☐ Send me a sample text.

☐ I shouldn't have done that - what was I thinking of? Thank God I'd already taken the 'fuck off' option because it means I don't have to return this form. Only those who have ticked box 9 are legally obliged to return it.

☐ By engaging, entertaining and enchanting me - the wonderful reader.

☐ By flattering me (though 'wonderful' may be overdoing it) to return this form.

○ That's enough boxes.

(Or make another box and tick that.)

THE MESSENGER

Up early. John is giving me a lift to Edinburgh from our parents' house in Perthshire and he appears a minute before we are due to go. I say goodbye to Dad – matter-of-fact but warm – and to Mum – hanging back a little since we kissed – and I get into the car. Tears in my eyes. So there should be, perhaps: the silver-haired man and the golden-haired woman are in their seventies and it will be months before I see them again. I look straight ahead and try to compose myself.

Blue summer's day. We swish along the clear roads. John sips from the large spill-proof beaker of coffee that is his constant travelling accessory on his constant travelling between Glasgow, Edinburgh, Manchester, London and Blair.

The radio is playing. A pair of DJs talk inanely but brightly in between records dripping with youth, energy, irreverence. I ask what we're listening to. John tells me as the daft lads phone (by arrangement: the piss-taking is gentle and everyone is in on it) a 'star guest'. They ask him questions about his group's recent records and public appearances. Where was the band playing on Monday, 12 May? The musician is certain it was

Leeds. But he is gleefully informed that it was Croydon. John and I both laugh as the countryside flashes past us.

It's nine-thirty when John pulls up close to his office. No melancholia as we take leave of each other – we'll be in touch soon enough. Indeed, I feel remarkably fresh and positive as, disdaining buses, I march south along Leith Walk towards the centre of the city whose grey granite stone walls are glistening in the morning sun.

Dark and cool and empty in the Fruitmarket Gallery, where Bill Viola's video *The Messenger* is showing on a large wall-screen. The figure of a man gradually emerges from the depths of a pool of water that the viewer is looking down upon. Breaking the surface, his eyes open and he releases a long-held breath in an explosion of sound that ends the silence. He breathes in and out, in slow motion, his eyes wide open. Then he inhales deeply and sinks back into the depths, his body losing definition until it is a wavering patch of light in an inky-black void.

I keep watching. And gradually the body is forming again, though, seen through the water, limbs are twisted unrecognizably... Recognizable as arms and legs now, though: the naked man, body blue-white, limbs straightening out, rising towards me... Hair swirls close to skull, eyes tight shut, arms at forty-five degrees to the body, this rising body... Wait for it... wait for it... Suddenly eyes open and breath out and muffled roar. I decide to count the breaths he takes... One... Stomach falling then rising... Two... Hair has fanned out over the water, framing the face differently from when immersed... Three... Genitals aren't in shot now that he is floating on the surface, closest to the camera, perhaps out of respect for the sensibilities... Four... of visitors to Durham Cathedral, which commissioned the work and where it was originally shown... Five... So who is this man?... Six... Christ, obviously. His coming and going; his suffering on the cross... Seven... Everyman, also. His life and death; his self-awareness... Eight...

The eighth breath is held and down he goes again. Trail of bubbles, hair skull-hugging, legs in shot once more, all descending... The body is losing definition – I couldn't say

188

those trails were arms and legs... And now the light patch could be anything: the Milky Way... Goodbye.

I walk up Calton Hill. My original intention was to mount Arthur's Seat, but John persuaded me I wouldn't get much time up there if I was to make the one o'clock train to London – which my ticket says I must do.

There is a grand view in all directions over the city, which looks glorious. Which way should I face? I sit looking north and my eye retraces my footsteps along Leith Walk in reverse towards the Forth estuary. Sunshine on Leith: I hope John is enjoying his Civil Service as I extract the lunch from my pack.

What has Mum (I couldn't stop her making them for me) put in my rolls? Corned beef and tomato; corned beef and green olives; tomato and olives. I bite into the first roll, chew the succulent combination of ingredients and swallow. Sudden surge of feeling. Great breaths of air for the second time today, this time unrestrained. Why such gulps?... My body has reacted to intense emotion by preparing itself for action: pumping adrenalin and blood. The blood needs oxygen and my lungs instinctively – insistently – take it.

Calm again. Breathing normally, I get on with the day.

To Frith Street to look again at a piece of work by Cornelia Parker.

From the gallery wall a white shelf protrudes at chest height. On this plinth sit twelve similar glasses – three or four inches tall, straight-sided and whose area at rim is only slightly greater than at base. Six of the glasses are stacked to form a near-vertical column which throws a Leaning Tower of Pisa-like shadow on to the wall. Each glass has a single word etched into it so that the column reads from top to bottom: ONE, DAY, THIS, GLASS, WILL, BREAK.

The other six glasses feature the same words arranged in a less obviously patterned way. DAY stacks on top of BREAK, but the remaining glasses are separate, perhaps arranged at random over the shelf, though with each word facing the viewer.

I look again at the tower. One day that tower will topple, smashing most of the first set of tumblers and perhaps taking others on to the floor too. Say only a couple of glasses survive. The whole sentence still stands: one day this glass will break. I take photos while I can...

•

I'm sitting at home with six glasses on the table in front of me. When I saw them for sale, looking basically the same as the gallery tumblers and priced so cheaply, I couldn't not have bought them.

One glass has something in it: a green cube with white spots on it. A single dice: a die. It makes a noise as I shake it around in the tumbler, then a different sound before it rolls to a stop on the table-top. A three. 'This'. I keep throwing; it is an elimination game I'm playing:

One day glass will break... One day will break... One day will... Day will... Day.

I must do that again. Starting with... a five.

One day this glass break... One day this break... One this break... This break... This.

Again...

Day this glass will break. Day this will break. Day this will. Day Will. Day.

Day this glass will break. Day this glass break. Day this break. Day break. Break.

One day this will break. One day this break. One day this. One this. This.

One day this glass will. One day glass will. One day will. One day. One.

I stop throwing the die and survey the table-top. The six glasses remain unbroken.

•

At the kitchen table, six glasses before me. I place a die in each glass, fill the glasses with cold water and place them in the ice-box of the fridge at five-minute intervals.

Later. The six dice are embedded in ice, though there is an air bubble and liquid in the middle of the two glasses that have been freezing for the shortest time.

Later. All glasses well and truly solid. The ice is smoky towards the centre of the glasses so that uppermost faces of dice can't be seen. No glass is cracked. I place the glasses – upside-down – on the top shelf of an oven set at 200 degrees centigrade.

Noise. I open the oven door. No dice have fallen but water is dripping from the glasses. Clatter. The first dice has dropped through the shelves to the black oven floor. The smokiness of the ice prevent me from reading the number of spots on the top face of the die. More clatter. I keep a note of the order in which the ice blocks fall.

Ice has melted; spots are exposed. Five, three, one, three, two, one. Building up the sentence 'Will this one this day one'.

I use oven gloves to extract the vessels. Thirty-eight years old and all my glasses intact.

WILL THIS ONE THIS DAY ONE.

I drop them in a basin of cold water. Pushing forty and not a single glass cracked.

WILL THIS ONE THIS DAY ONE.

Q. How do I carry on with this book I'm writing about contemporary visual art?

A. (Tick box or boxes.)

☑ Depends what sort of book it is. But in any case...

☐ By going to exhibitions, engaging with the ideas and aesthetics of the artist, and responding imaginatively. (As perhaps you have been.)

☐ By asking editors, artists, bus drivers, friends, gallerists, literary agents, landscape gardeners and tattooists.

☑ Don't ask me.

☐ By listening to barking dogs, closing doors, passing cars and running water.

☑ By working out your motivation for producing this document.

☑ Don't give yourself a hard time - just go for it.

☐ Don't bother.

☐ "GO FOR IT, DUNC!"

☐ Nothing could persuade me to tick that last box.

☑ I'm tempted to tick the next box though.

☐ FUCK OFF.

☐ I shouldn't have done that - it seems a bit harsh. How would I like it if I sent out 200 copies of a carefully worded form and the only ones to come back told me to fuck off?

☐ Send me a list of artists whose work you've written about so far.

☐ Send me a sample text.

☐ I shouldn't have done that - what was I thinking of? Thank God I'd already taken the 'fuck off' option because it means I don't have to return this form. Only those who have ticked box 9 are legally obliged to return it.

☐ By engaging, entertaining and enchanting me - the wonderful reader.

☐ By flattering me (though 'wonderful' may be overdoing it) to return this form.

◯ That's enough boxes.

(Or make another box and tick that.)

☑ POUR ANOTHER GLASS! Good luck
R.

20:50

Richard Wilson's 20:50 is a permanent installation at Saatchi's. Asked by the guard not to touch the waist-high sides of the metal gangway, I follow Joanna into the room.

It feels like walking the plank – high above the floor. In fact the room contains used sump oil (Joanna tells me that 20:50 is the name of a brand of engine oil) and we are standing in a narrow corridor cut into it, the only part of the huge room which isn't liquid up to waist level.

The 'floor' is a reflection of the ceiling. I suppose that the same effect could be created by fitting a tinted mirror horizontally from wall to wall. Joanna points out that you couldn't get a single mirror big enough; there would have to be joins, spoiling the perfection of the effect. And the piece is perfect. My eye follows the unwavering horizon from the nearest wall all the way to the far wall. My eye travels back through the middle of the room, dipping and leaping for want of anything – not a ripple – to latch on to. Not a liquid, surely. But I dip a finger into the surface beyond the side of the corridor and it's liquid sure enough. I watch a drop of the grey drip back into itself.

If we were alone, I would lie down on the causeway. Perhaps Joanna would lie down with me. The guard keeps watch, but no matter. If we were alone, we could lie down together on the causeway. By some miracle protected from the void all around us.

One Day This Glass Will Break. Joanna and I no longer protected from the void – lying under it. No longer differentiated from the void – part of it. No trace anywhere of life.

NESTBOX

Carl von Weiler has built *Nest* in excavated and reopened spaces alongside his studio in the basement of an industrial building in east London.

I sit down on a chair and observe the round-shouldered shadow cast on corridor floorboards by the naked bulb above the door. Straightening my back, I look through the slot into the space beyond, which seems to be a darkened room. Cool air blows on to my face.

Floorboards – the floor has been built up to the level of the slot – lead my gaze to the far wall of the room, which contains a small window. Light from it is insufficient for me to make out the boundaries of the room or to tell how it is furnished. A machine hums in the far left corner, perhaps a fan. Maybe the cold air I feel against my face comes in through the window and is blown across the room by an unseen fan.

My gaze is channelled towards the back of the room by the bottom of a bed above as well as by floorboards below. One long edge of the bed must be set against the other side of the corridor wall, its underside a few inches above the top of the

199

slot. I rise from the chair in order to put my arm through the slot and investigate the bed. There isn't a bedspread. I don't know if there is a pillow but I can feel a mattress. Smooth, curved legs on castors. Just an ordinary bed as far as I can make out. I relax back into the chair, cool air on my forehead.

Staring straight ahead, I realize that the underside of the bed prevents me from seeing the top part of the window. I rise from the chair again in order to place my face hard against the slot, from where I can see the entire window plus more of the room. My eyes must be fully adjusted to the low light conditions by now and I don't think there is anything else in there apart from the machine in the corner, which traces of a circle suggest is indeed a fan. Blowing cold air from the outside world under the bed, against my skin and along the corridor.

I go with the flow. As I approach the wider wooden chamber my shadow disappears. Looking back, I see it behind me – cast by the bare bulb in the centre of the ceiling of the space I'm now entering. Which seems empty except for the roughly hewn, home-made bed, which nearly fills it. I sit on the mattress, raise my legs, swing them across and rest them down. And I lower my back until it also is supported.

There is no pillow; my head rests upon the mattress. The bulb above me is not a powerful one, so it feels comfortable enough looking up, with eyes only slightly averted. My eyes keep moving though, along the wooden boards of the ceiling, then down those of the wall. Back and forth my gaze travels without coming across anything other than the wooden boards. I turn on to my front, my hands meeting above my head at the top of the mattress. This lumpy mattress. Fingers succeed in isolating a single lump under the close-woven cover. I squeeze the lump, which crumbles into two or more pieces. Is it earth? Am I lying on an earth mattress? I rather think that I am...

A sound wakes me. From directly overhead I hear muffled footsteps. Now to the right, descending and fainter... Silence. Until I hear the footfalls coming back... ascending and getting louder... no sooner overhead than gone. I wonder who made the return journey and why.

Turning on to my right, one wall is close enough to touch. My hand moves out to stroke the grain but it stops between the edge of the bed and the wall upon encountering rising warm air. I put my head over the other edge of the bed so as to freely investigate below. Hot air on my face now. The source of it is a heater – two long tubes – on the floorboards directly under the centre of the bed. I draw back, out of the flow, and consider the warm air rising on all sides of me. Presumably it piles up at the ceiling. But the air pressure can't build up indefinitely. Some of the warm air must get pushed down and out of the chamber to make its way back along the corridor. Not nearly as strong a current as the one of cold air towards the chamber, so I don't follow it. I'm comfortable here...

Sound wakes me again. That same return journey. How often have I heard it?

I rise, walk along the corridor, sit down on the chair and look through the slot into the darkened room beyond. Under the bed lies a white envelope with my name and address on it, a green stamp – top right – and a code number – 085 – in the opposite corner. I close my eyes. Fresh air blows on to my face. Nostrils draw it down into lungs.

This envelope is from Carl von Weiler. I tear it open (gently, gently) and find myself staring at my returned questionnaire:

Q.   How do I carry on with this book I'm writing about contemporary visual art?

A.   (Tick box or boxes.)

☐   Depends what sort of book it is. But in any case...

☐   By going to exhibitions, engaging with the ideas and aesthetics of the
      artist, and responding imaginatively. (As perhaps you have been.)

☐   By asking editors, artists, bus drivers, friends, gallerists, literary
      agents, landscape gardeners and tattooists.

☐   Don't ask me.

☐   By listening to barking dogs, closing doors, passing cars and running water.

☑   By working out your motivation for producing this document.

☐   Don't give yourself a hard time - just go for it.

☐   Don't bother.

☐   "GO FOR IT, DUNC!"

☐   Nothing could persuade me to tick that last box.

☐   I'm tempted to tick the next box though.

☐   FUCK OFF.

☐   I shouldn't have done that - it seems a bit harsh. How would I like it if I
      sent out 200 copies of a carefully worded form and the only ones to come back
      told me to fuck off?

☐   Send me a list of artists whose work you've written about so far.

☐   Send me a sample text.

☐   I shouldn't have done that - what was I thinking of? Thank God I'd already
      taken the 'fuck off' option because it means I don't have to return this
      form. Only those who have ticked box 9 are legally obliged to return it.

☐   By engaging, entertaining and enchanting me - the wonderful reader.

☐   By flattering me (though 'wonderful' may be overdoing it) to return this form.

◯   That's enough boxes.

      (Or make another box and tick that.)

A single tick has been quite a common response from artists. Bob Smith ticked 'GO FOR IT, DUNC!'. Cornelia Parker ticked 'By listening to barking dogs, closing doors, passing cars and running water.' Both Matthew Higgs and David Shrigley went for 'Don't give yourself a hard time – just go for it.' And Douglas Gordon drew a large box on the back of the form, which he ticked. and which reads, 'CHANGE YOUR NAME TO "MALCOLM": YOU'LL SELL LOADS, MAKE A FORTUNE AND IT DON'T HAVE TO BE GOOD.'

I walk along the corridor to the chamber, reach under the bed and extract the box of returned questionnaires. I add Carl's to the hundred-high pile – attaching form to envelope with a paperclip. Then I make an entry in my 'Questionnaire Diary'.

As often before, I open the box again and scrutinize the anonymous reply. Both questionnaire and SAE have been mutilated. The code number has been cut out of the envelope, creating a window box. The sentence '(Or make another box and tick that)' has been cut from the questionnaire and stuck inside the envelope in such a way that '(Or make' is visible through the cut window. This is the most novel ticked box I've received. For a while I thought it was from Dave Willshaw, creator of 'Bearded Baby'. But I now think it may have come from someone else. Does it matter? I thought it did, but I'm not sure that I care any more.

I lie down on the bed. My cheek, my knees and my hip explore mattress before finding comfortable hollows. Earth turns to dust in the process, everything disintegrates and suddenly (after how many months?) I have had enough of Questionnaire.

I'm getting out of here tomorrow; I'm leaving this behind.

The Cable Street Gallery

566 Cable Street, Limehouse, London E1 9HB   Phone/Fax: 0171-790 1309

PRESS RELEASE

"CAN'T SEE THE WOOD FOR THE TREES"

Twelve artists brought together under the thematic umbrella of panic and confusion.

The show explores issues relating to the imposition of order - whether generated by, or imposed upon, the artist. In responding to disorder, the artists engage with a range of emotions from uneasiness to abject terror, from whisper to roar.

The show runs from 14 Feb - 9 March, 1997; open Thurs-Sun 12.00-6.00 p.m.

Working in the divide between the apparent and the obscure, the artists use a range of media and materials - from wax to helium, sugar to sound, plasticine to video, pigment to photography.

Alex Schady makes animal tails; **Nicholas Symes** asks us to accept the unacceptable. **Kate Carrick**'s work explores the breakdown of the food chain; **Tony Peakall** presents builders' rubble in considering social and historical equality. **Rosemary Smith** works site-specifically on walls with tentative drawings; **Anthony Shapland** gives gravity to the situation. **Jo Bennett** explores issues of anxiety and control; **Simon Marshall** asks "Who came first ?" **Steve Thompson** plays with the rectangular 2-D format; **Mary Kirk** investigates seduction and repulsion. **Jon Wright** finds histories in the shell of a cracked nut; **Rochelle Fry** makes up stories with no meaning.

From the relationship between these diverse works, the viewer is invited to create a sense of order...

WOOD FOR THE TREES

I'm standing in front of a turquoise rabbit hutch. To one side, where there'd normally be view of hutch interior behind wire mesh, there's a TV screen. Behind the closed turquoise door of the other half there's a video player. No rabbit. I know this because I helped Joanna assemble the piece for the group show 'Can't See the Wood for the Trees' which I've just walked round.

The video shows a table with two place settings for a formal meal. Facing the camera is the black-dressed torso of a woman. To the left, side on, sits the second diner, whose hands are the only part of him in shot except when his white-sleeved arm stretches for something. The table is agleam with cutlery and glasses. The pair are eating and drinking though there is neither food nor drink. As they mime their way through the breaking and buttering of bread rolls, it appears that she is teaching him table manners. I know this to be so because I'm the student. There is a rabbit of sorts, then.

Soup. Joanna demonstrates how to hold the spoon correctly and how to move it. Away from one. Pause to let the soup cool – that's why the spoon head is wide and shallow. Spoon to mouth, not vice versa. In between mouthfuls, let the spoon rest on the plate supporting the bowl. I pick up the spoon again and Joanna explains what is wrong with the way I am holding it. I concentrate hard; I do my best. She tells me that I must learn to relax and to chat as I go along. I pour us both a glass of wine and take a good old slurp from the dry white imaginary.

The fish course. Apparently there are Dover soles with slices of lemon on the silver platter; Joanna transfers them to our plates. Picking up the ornate cutlery, I'm told that these implements are made from lower-grade silver than the rest of the silver service since fish oils and citric acid tarnish pure metal. I lay my fancy knife and fork – prongs down, blade in – on the plate as I chew my food and think about what Joanna's just said. She urges me to make polite conversation. Why don't I talk to her about the other works in the show?

I describe an exhibit: babies made of bread emerging from a cupboard, following a line of rats which have been cast from... I'm not sure what... and streaked with icing sugar.

'What do you make of Kate's work?' asks Joanna, discreetly removing a fish bone from her mouth under cover of napkin.

'My first thoughts were of innocence being led by – or turning into – the base, deceitful or hypocritical. Then I saw the work is titled *Three Blind Mice*. The only line of the nursery rhyme I could remember was 'cut off their tails with a carving knife'. But in trying to recall more I thought of another children's story – *The Pied Piper* – which features rats (definitely) being piped out of town, and children (I think) following.'

'Will you follow up these references?'

'Sure. I want to remind myself of the stories for their own sake, and I assume they'll enable me to get more out of Kate's work.'

Joanna has finished her fish and placed her knife and fork (prongs up) together on the side of her plate. She sips from her wine, asks me if I know about Kate's diet and reminds me not to sit brandishing knife and fork in between mouthfuls.

I lay down my cutlery and ask about the artist's diet.

'She can't eat wheat or sugar products. They've made her

very ill in the past. It's not surprising that her work deals with breakdown of the food chain.'

I nod slowly. I picture a sugar-coated rat which I'm holding in my hand all of a sudden. I give it a tentative lick on the rump. No problem. I lick the sweetness from its back, its chest, its armpits. Still no negative side-effects. Caution gone, I lick the rat's head, its snout, its ears. There's still some sugary-sweet in its shell-like but my tongue is too blunt an instrument to extract more. Just my luck if that's where the E-numbers have gone to ground...

A voice tells me that if I've finished I should move my cutlery. I drop the rat and adopt the position.

Main course. Joanna serves the meat – fillet steak in a rich sauce – and holds the vegetable dish for me to serve myself with peas, celery and new potatoes. Then I hold the dish, turning it round so that the handle of the serving spoon is towards her.

Joanna asks me to pour the red wine. Guided by her, I hold the bottle in my left hand, supporting its neck with a napkin held in my right. I pour into first one large glass – not too much, Joanna explains that the vessel is capacious so as to collect the bouquet – then the other, using the napkin to soak up the drip of wine running down the dark bottle's neck.

I savour the bouquet for a few seconds' breathing space. I hold the large knife and fork in the accepted manner, though self-consciously. I eat and I drink passably well once Joanna has explained to me about the forks and the peas. But not in silence, Joanna reminds me: talk.

I mention Simon's piece in the show. An array of twelve chickens (two each of blue, green, yellow, pink, orange and reddy-brown) lying on butcher's grass inside and filling a child's playpen, the bars of which are painted the same colours as the glossy chickens.

'Similar elements to Kate's work – animals, children and food,' comments Joanna, piling peas on to the back of her fork.

'And he's called it *Who killed Cock Robin?*'

Joanna explains and justifies the convention of not talking

with one's mouth full, then adds, 'Another nursery rhyme I can't quite remember.'

I do recall the gist of it. A series of birds, including owl, swan and rook, deny responsibility for the killing. Then the house sparrow chirps up at the end with a frank acceptance of responsibility which puts the others to shame.

> 'I,' said the sparrow
> 'With my bow and arrow,
> I killed Cock Robin.'

Joanna takes exception to my description of the other birds as 'fucking hypocrites'. I admit that I don't know why I used such language. She expounds the view that dinner-table talk should be judged so as to aid the digestion: polite and soothing. Not boring, hopefully, but nothing too controversial either. And certainly nothing gratuitously vulgar.

She goes on to recite an anecdote involving Kate's and Simon's curation of the show, which I would listen to if I wasn't being so insistently distracted by imagery...

I've got hold of a plaster chicken painted glossy green. It's smooth and cold and heavy and I'm going to see how much wine I can pour into the parson's nose. I hug the bird to my chest as I tilt the bottle... There – a bloody good glassful. Carefully, with both hands, I lift the chicken to my face. I savour the bouquet, but not for too long because there's something wrong with it. Gulp. I lower the chicken, but if I was to rest it on the table then the remainder of its wine would slip away, so it's up to my mouth again to drain that chicken dry. It grows a head on the end of a long neck.

> 'Not I,' said the swan,
> 'I'm sorry he's gone.
> I'll miss poor Cock Robin.'

'Duncan!' says a voice, startling me. I drop the bird on to the floor, where it explodes into white fragments. I pull myself together.

Dessert. *Crêpe Suzette*. What is that? Pancake served with orange and brandy sauce. I pick up the last of my forks and the dessert spoon and I... hesitate. Joanna shows the way forward.

I describe another exhibit: a child's tricycle with motorcycle wing mirrors attached to its tiny handlebars so that a rider could see on either side of the blue and pink mottled screen which is attached to the back of the trike with plastic chains. I was told that the screen is a replica of the one used to separate male and female contestants on *Blind Date*, and the sculpture made sense. But not so for Joanna, who has never seen the programme. I cut the pancake with the edge of my spoon and transfer a morsel from plate to mouth via fork, but now it's me leading the way.

I ask Joanna to imagine she's sitting on the tricycle. She looks in the handlebar mirrors and sees a young man. 'Hi, I'm Alan. I like to go out with my mates almost as much as I look forward to a hot date. How would *you* help me strike a balance in my social life?' Alan adds that he wants to hear A's answer first. I advise Joanna to look in her other wing mirror – the one that allows you to look up three girls' skirts. 'Hi, Alan, I'm Suzette and nothing would give me more pleasure than to be fucked by you in your local pub, surrounded by your envious friends, while I panted sweet nothings along the lines of, 'Oh, that's it; that's wonderful; you're wonderful, Alan; Alan, you're the man...'

Dismounting without waiting to hear B's or C's answer, Joanna complains about the tricycle's restrictive dimensions. I use spoon alone to tackle the sauce, lapping it up in my mind's eye.

The cheeseboard. I pass the silver dish that contains biscuits and Joanna takes two, as is traditional. She picks up the cheeseknife, uses the blade to cut a slice of Brie – not chopping off the end but leaving it wedge-shaped as before – and uses the blade to carry the slice on to her side plate. She also cuts a piece of Cheddar, using the double point of the knife to stab the cheese and transfer it to plate. I cut and carry a slice of Gorgonzola; cut and stab a piece of Stilton.

I mention the exhibit which consists of builders' rubble in plastic buckets. Alongside the row of buckets is a list of London addresses – houses in Hackney, Crouch End, Belgravia, Camberwell, Mayfair – and the implication that a bucket of rubble has been collected from each address.

Is rubble from Belgravia more valuable than Hackney rubble? Of course not. Would it matter if the artist had filled all the buckets with crumbling bricks and mortar from his own backyard? I hope he did just that. I hope he's got a system of proving that the buckets are identifiable. (Joanna confirms this, each bucket has a number stuck underneath it.) I hope he's got a notebook/diary of his visits to the houses, containing interviews with householders, permissions to remove material and details of where the samples were taken. And I hope that it's all bollocks.

There's no faking this Gorgonzola, though. I cut myself another slice, take a piece of jagged mortar from the Camberwell...no, the Mayfair bucket, get rid of the dust by tapping the cement sharply with knife over napkin, and use my lips, teeth and tongue to detach the soft, damp and delicious from the hard, dry and inedible.

More cheese. First, a rat liberally smeared with runny-ripe Camembert. Second, a chicken firmly stuffed with Greek Feta. I lean back, grossly full, suddenly and uncomfortably aware that the cheese I've eaten would fill a bucket and that every scrap of it was a mild, pale, pasteurized Cheddar. I feel such an idiot.

Toilet break. Joanna asks me not to be long for the sake of video continuity. I reassure her on that point as I carefully slide back my chair and slip away from it – all out of camera.

Awaiting bowel movement. In a corner of the loo is a wall drawing. Vivid ultramarine pigment and black charcoal have been used. Much of it lies in heaps and trails on the floor, but that which has been applied to the walls is suggestive of a journey.

I start low on the wall to the right, where the main motif occurs in its largest form. Tubular poles with horizontal bars, perhaps, the kind of barrier found throughout London's underground network, to control the flow of people. Small versions of these go up the wall, into the corner from where a pylon-flanked railway line seems to emerge. This goes so far along the left wall, then there is a vertical drop, a single black line, towards the floor. Splodges and streaks of screaming blue and black. End of circuit.

So here I am sitting comfortably, contemplating a journey. Have I just arrived at the office in the morning? Have I newly returned home after a hard day's work? To answer, I'd have to sit longer considering the three intersecting planes of this 'canvas'. What do 'up' and 'down' mean here? How do I interpret moving into and out of the corner? And I'd have to follow the circuit in reverse a few times. But I can't do any of this because where I actually am (or should be) is in the middle of a dinner I must be getting back to. Bowel movement. As I defecate I'm wondering if the artist has read *The Lost Ones* by Samuel Beckett.

I make conventional use of the toilet roll, finish the job with a single sheet of moistened tissue and look round the rest of the strangely appointed washroom. The door is covered by a thick curtain of Plasticine. I had to push it about to effect an entry and the rigmarole will have to be repeated when I leave, but it is not an unpleasant experience. Hands on clammy, waxy, means to an end.

Tails are mounted on the walls: lions' tails. The male's has a tuft on the end; the three females' are longer and have an extra twirl to them. A pride of Baroque banister ends.

And what's this on the floor? Paper bags made from pages from broadsheet newspapers stand upside-down. I pick up one to see how it's made. A wide, thin bag with neat folds and tucks. I think of chemists' bags when my eye falls on a flat disc on the floor near the display: a powder compact.

But it's not eyeshadow according to the folded-up piece of literature next to it. The powder is bright yellow and a single external application keeps the anus open and fresh for up to twenty-four hours – about the life of a cut sunflower in full bloom.

I'm not sure which finger I should apply the powder with. No doubt there is strict etiquette on the subject, but Joanna is not around to keep me straight. Maybe I can work it out from first principles. I spread the fingers of my right hand. The index finger is tipped ultramarine where I made my contribution to the wall drawing. So surely it is the ring finger that needs tipping yellow if an aesthetic balance is to be achieved. Fourth finger it is, then... And I feel my tight arse opening as sweetly as a daffodil trumpet at this time of year.

Better return to dining room. As I approach the Plasticine drape, it simply disappears: an automatic dissolving door. I didn't even need to say 'Open Sunflower'. I stand there aghast in admiration.

Joanna doesn't seem to mind that I've been absent for so long. She tells me that she's stopped the tape but that if I sit back she'll restart it with the remote control and no one will be any the wiser.

Coffee and brandy. There is only one small cup-and-saucer, so I offer it to Joanna. But she wants me to have it for compositional reasons, so I place it on the table accordingly. Then the image of me knocking the other cup-and-saucer from kitchen worktop to floor, where it shattered earlier in the day, comes to mind. And, stupidly, I lift the surviving crockery and offer it again to Joanna. I hear my name hissed from behind clenched teeth.

We both have brandy glasses. Joanna shows me how to hold the balloon: with fingers and palm spread around the bottom, heating the alcohol, the bulk of the glass confining the fumes. She moves her glass in horizontal circles and sniffs at it. I follow suit.

Joanna tells me about alternatives to brandy – liqueurs in tiny glasses; passing the port from the left – but then she dries up. I really want this meal to succeed, so I make an effort to resume conversation. I describe to Joanna – who hasn't seen them – the pair of photos that constitute *Portscape*.

The first photo shows two near-identical picnic spreads in a field. The second shows a man in the foreground, dressed in a suit, most of his head out of frame; behind him the same man (wearing the same tie, anyway) in a graduation portrait where again (but for no logical reason this time) the top of his head is missing.

That's rather a dense description, but Joanna seems to have followed it. Her hand cups her brandy, making gentle swirling actions as if beckoning me to continue.

Back to the first photo: a vertical edge of the nearest picnic rug is out of frame bottom right. This is echoed in the distant picnic rug which has been set out in such a way as to create a hard vertical right edge from the camera's point of view. Fun with the rectangular format of the picture frame. But more than that.

I look down at my brandy. Swirl. Am I going to get away with talking about another exhibit in conjunction with this last? Sip. The tongue set free...

Magic Man: a hamper-sized closed box; empty plastic glasses; Plasticine worms (coloured, striped, spotted; hand-rolled) in a rough line leading to a child's football; a cardboard cutout of a moustachioed man's head and shoulders. The whole suggestive of shadows, ghosts, echoes.

Together *Portscape* and *Magic Man* conjure up a memory of picnic past. Five of us dressed in academic gowns and bow ties sitting on a chequered rug in a field near Cambridge. Free-flowing red wine; *Blind Date* standard repartee; the langour of youth. I fell asleep and awoke an hour later, give or take fifteen years. Anyway, my peers had gone.

I noticed a trail of worms over the picnic rug (I'm so obviously making this up). The worms were heading for a pork pie I'd really fancied earlier. I went to save the pie, but from the new angle it seemed that the worms were radiating from it. I decided to give said pie a miss, regardless of use-by date.

More worms, zeroing in on the hamper. But of course that was wrong and I didn't fancy opening the box merely to confirm my new theory. Late afternoon chill – abandon picnic. Early evening gloom – go home and grow up before it's too late.

'But it was too late,' I finish melodramatically, draining the last of my brandy.

Joanna tells me that we can stand up from the table – our meal is complete. 'Not until we've had the *pièce de résistance*,' says a voice – mine, perhaps. 'Bring on the singing walnut.'

It's bigger than a football, made of aluminium, and there are holes out of which two metal tubes protrude. It's a walnut all right, nothing could be more obvious, but with one unusual quality. I invite Joanna to listen in.

She puts her ear to the listening tube pointing her way. I persuade her to change ears so that she's facing me. And I use my right ear against the other tube so that I'm facing her. See how that makes sense! The very epitome of civilization – face to face while listening to the singing walnut. Not singing exactly. Not singing so much as sighing, breathing (in, out; in, out; in, out), laughing.

Joanna seems distressed. I ask what's wrong but she won't say. I persist and finally she admits that she's afraid the walnut's laughing at her. But the nut's not laughing *at* anyone. It reminds me of the laughing policeman, laughing for two distinct reasons: from sheer *joie de vivre* and because he's an out-and-out nutter.

Joanna is still upset. Now she claims it's me that's laughing at her. But I'm only smiling. And I'm not smiling at Joanna but at what the walnut's just said: 'I'm so hungry, my stomach thinks my throat's been fist-fucked.' Not funny really, so I stop smiling.

Joanna's calmed down. She'd like the video to run for another few minutes so that the camera's ninety-minute tape is complete. All she'll do then is copy it twice on to a three-hour VCR tape. Which means that in a six-hour gallery invigilation the video will have to be restarted only once.

We agree to leave the table. The last scene can be the table-top with our crumpled napkins and the singing walnut and nothing else. We leave the table.

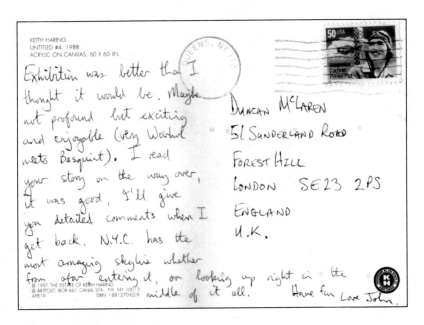

KEITH HARING
UNTITLED #4, 1988
ACRYLIC ON CANVAS, 60 X 60 IN.

Exhibition was better than I thought it would be. Maybe not profound but exciting and enjoyable (very Warhol meets Basquiat). I read your story on the way over, it was good, I'll give you detailed comments when I get back. N.Y.C. has the most amazing skyline whether from afar entering it, or looking up right in the middle of it all. Have fun Love John.

DUNCAN McLAREN
51 SUNDERLAND ROAD
FOREST HILL
LONDON   SE23 2PS
ENGLAND
U.K.

© 1997 THE ESTATE OF KEITH HARING
© ARTPOST, BOX 661 CANAL STA., NY, NY 10013
APR 19   ISBN 1-881270-02-9

Postcard from my brother.

'Exhibition was better than I thought it would be.' Fine, but what exhibition does he mean?

'I read your story on the way over, it was good.' Great, but I've sent him 'Strange Child', 'Real Life vs. Nature', 'Edinburgh Man' and 'The Messenger'...'

Postcard from Joanna's father

'Very many thanks for the typescript of 'Can't see...'. Much enjoyed reading it and greatly admired the good, clean prose and the tight control you kept over your presentation of your imaginative flights. Without the control the reader would have been lost?'

No time to dwell on that now – Joanna's solo show closes soon. This time I'm making sure of not losing the reader by inviting a couple of them along...

jo bennett
DISPLACEMENT

28 Feb-23 March 1997
open Fri-Sun 2-6 pm

Down Stairs
50 Tasman Rd London
SW9 9PA

private view
Sun 23 Feb 6-8 pm

jo bennett
DISPLACEMEN

28 Feb-23 March 1997
open Fri-Sun 2-6 pm

Down Stairs
50 Tasman Rd London
SW9 9PA

private view
Sun 23 Feb 6-8 pm

jo bennett
DISPLACEMENT

28 Feb-23 March 1997
open Fri-Sun 2-6 pm

Down Stairs
50 Tasman Rd London
SW9 9PA

private view
Sun 23 Feb 6-8 pm

jo bennett
DISPLACEMEN

28 Feb-23 March 1997
open Fri-Sun 2-6 pm

Down Stairs
50 Tasman Rd London
SW9 9PA

private view
Sun 23 Feb 6-8 pm

jo bennett
DISPLACEMENT

28 Feb-23 March 1997
open Fri-Sun 2-6 pm

Down Stairs
50 Tasman Rd London
SW9 9PA

private view
Sun 23 Feb 6-8 pm

jo bennett
DISPLACEMEN

28 Feb-23 March 199
open Fri-Sun 2-6 pm

Down Stairs
50 Tasman Rd London
SW9 9PA

private view
Sun 23 Feb 6-8 pm

DISPLACEMENT

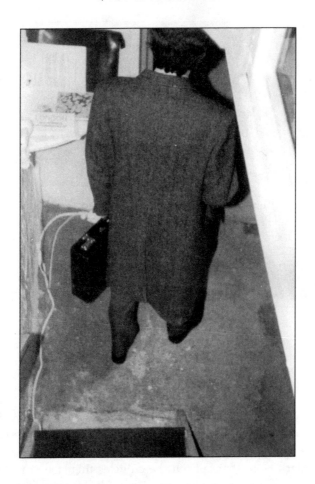

Richard and Mark have travelled here after work from Liverpool Street and Tower Hill, respectively. Richard has left his briefcase outside the basement gallery, beside press releases and visitors' book, and I suggest that Mark does the same. He hesitates before doing so; hesitates again before entering the gallery.

Concrete floor; grey-painted brick walls; a row of five cubicles. Each is lit by a single fluorescent striplight set vertically on the wall in front. The spacing of the lights is uneven due to irregularities in the wall but the cubicles themselves make no concessions to the architecture. They fill the space except for narrow corridors in front, behind and to one side; there is not room for a sixth. The visitor can't get any distance from the row, which is difficult to take in as a whole.

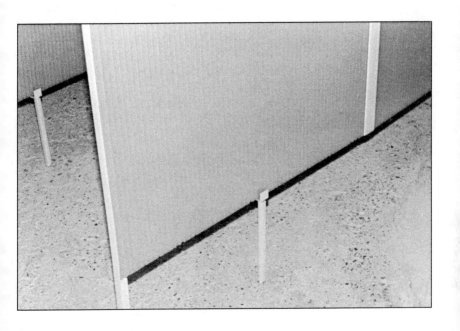

Each cubicle consists of five translucent polycarbonate sheets intended for use as conservatory roofing. There is a gap between bottom edge and floor, also between top edge and roof joists. Everything seems lined up, more or less; each plane seems securely supported, although there is an air of fragility to the installation. Standing inside a cubicle, lifting my arms, I touch both the long side-walls easily enough. How do I feel?... Oh, I know how I feel; I helped build the cubicles, have been familiar with them for weeks now. But today isn't about my reactions. How are Richard and Mark doing?

Glassy-eyed and staring off into neutral corners. I don't think they've engaged with the work, though I did tell them what to expect. Or rather I told them what not to expect – discrete art objects for discreet viewing.

Mark says that he feels like a pint. Richard wonders aloud how the trains are from Clapham. Both agree that they don't want to be late home tonight because of office commitments tomorrow. Pub, train, house, office – Mark and Richard would rather be anywhere else than this gallery. I want to tell them to *relax*, but I can't just say that and expect it to have the desired effect.

Joanna intercepts their escape. She talks about the work with
the same zest and commitment she's shown throughout the
project. An anecdote about the delivery of materials is followed
by another about the bungling of a detail of the construction.
My mistake, as it happens. Mark and Richard begin to show an
interest. I slip in between them to pick up a press release; slip
past again and into a cubicle. I read:

Jo Bennett explores the role of architectural devices in representing social structures in the broadest sense; themes of dislocation, anxiety and fractured communication recur in her work.

I stop reading when I realize that the same press release is being read aloud by Richard from the gallery doorway. I listen: 'In alluding to the relationship of the individual to structures of restraint and authority, the artist's concerns focus on exploring formal oppositions: specifically the division between public and private; autonomy and control.'

Silence. Keep quiet, Richard.

Richard's voice comes at me from above and below:
'Earlier work has used the door as representing the notion of
boundary within an anthropological space: the idea of territory
as an abstract, indefinite space, with journey narratives, has
been represented by physical barriers: a dysfunctional revolv-
ing door; an automatic sliding door built of cardboard.'
   Richard must be walking up and down the corridor behind
me, as he reads:
'In this, the first show at Down Stairs, the artist considers the
intimidating nature of lack of privacy within public spaces.
Although each person is designated their own space, each is
cramped together, affording minimal seclusion. The individual's vulnerability is made clearly visible.'

224

I emerge from cubicle to see how Richard and Mark have reacted to the press release. They seem to have come to an arrangement about territorial rights to cubicles two and three. It is obvious to me which of them feels comfortable enough with the situation to have posed for this photograph. But the beaming smile on Richard's face contrasts so glaringly with the woebegone expression on Mark's that I don't feel comfortable about capturing it on camera.

Richard fancies himself to be in the changing rooms of a department store – John Lewis's or Debenham's – trying on new suits. So the first thing is to get his old trousers off and discard them in a heap on the floor. Mark pays no attention to Richard's prattle or his actions, except to glance down to his right when a leg of Richard's trousers intrudes an inch or two into his own cubicle.

Richard's tie joins his trousers on the concrete floor but he hangs his jacket neatly from an imperfection along the top edge of cubicle wall. I ask why the jacket gets special attention. Richard shrugs. I ask why he's taken off his tie if it's a suit he's shopping for. Richard tells me he always buys a new silk tie to go with a new suit. And I ask why he has emerged from the cubicle. Richard tells me he is wearing new suit trousers and needs to see himself in the full-length mirror customarily found at the end of the cubicle corridor, so as to properly judge the cut of the trousers (very sexy) and the line (these are the sexiest things that Richard has worn in ages). Richard struts around in his shirt-tails.

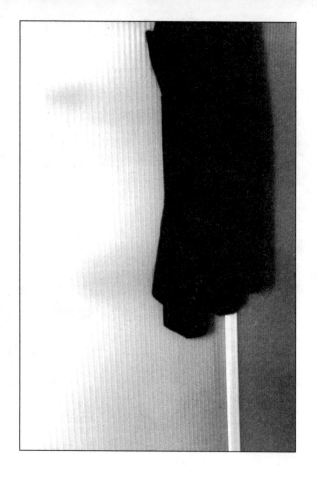

I take a closer look at Richard's jacket. So many buttons, pockets, collars, seams: all the workmanship immaculate, or so it appears to me. Richard tells me he wants a much lighter suit – in weight and colour – for sporting to the office this coming summer.

Leaving Richard trying on suits, I follow Mark round the back of the installation. He looks over the top of cubicle one, briefly standing on his toes, and tells me that Joanna is in there – meditating or something. He peers over the top of cubicle two and reports another peaceful scene – empty space. Cautiously, he looks over into cubicle three and – with relief in his voice – informs me that Richard is decent again.

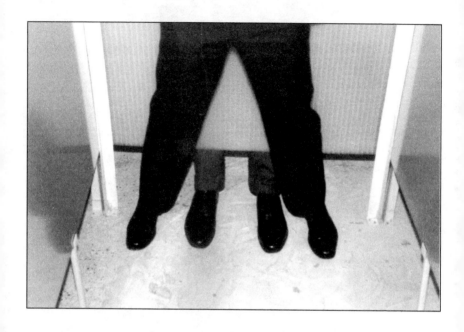

Richard asks Mark to stand hard against the back of his cubicle. Mark obliges and Richard demonstrates what a giant of a
man he is relative to tiny Mark. I'm not sure to what extent the
effect is psychological: Richard has become so expansive
whereas Mark has gone all introspective since engaging with
the installation.

Richard announces he's going to try on bigger suits – he needs the next size up as far as both waist and inside-leg measurements are concerned.

'Oh, stop going on about your bloody trousers,' says Mark, suddenly intimidated into protest.

'SUITS YOU, SIR!' says Richard, sticking his head under the cubicle divide. Mark is out of there like a startled rabbit.

'Was it something I said?' asks Richard. I reassure him it couldn't have been anything he'd said or done that had driven Mark from cubicle four to five.

Richard continues to support himself so that his clothes are kept clear of the concrete. 'Isn't that rather a strain?' I ask. I'm told that Richard got into the habit of doing 100 press-ups daily when he was working from home, and that although he's back in an office environment he's still fit.

Richard reminds me how much he disliked working from home. No proper work station, no banter with colleagues and no need to wear a suit. He made his phone calls – Richard sold insurance – dressed casually, but would pepper his conversation with allusions to a suit. A regular tactic when he needed time to come up with a strategy for clinching a sale was to say his pen/calculator/diary was in the jacket he'd left in a colleague's office.

Once Richard asked a client, who had phoned to update a personal pension scheme, to bear with him while he retrieved his pen, which had escaped via a hole in his pocket into the lining of his jacket. In fact, he'd gone upstairs to the loo, washed his face and hands and scrutinized his reflection in the mirror, while gripping his pen between nose and upper lip and considering whether he would suit a circus-master's waxed moustache.

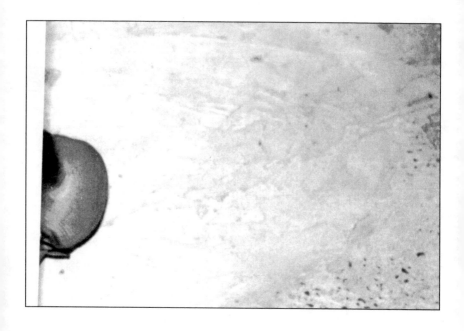

Richard wants to tell me about his new job. But he doesn't want to make Mark jealous, so he's going to speak softly. I crouch down towards the fourth cubicle and listen. An open-plan office; fluorescent lighting; a computer screen on every desk. On one side of Richard works a fifty-year-old Indian woman who is quieter than any mouse Richard has met. On the other side works an overweight young man whose shame complex makes it difficult for him to communicate in any meaningful way. Richard is working on both of them, principally via his 'thought for the day', which is transmitted through the building by e-mail.

This week's thoughts for the day have been taken from the *Rubáiyát of Omar Khayyám*. At nine a.m. on Monday, Richard entered into his PC:

> From that wine-jug which has no harm in it
> Fill a bowl, boy, drink and pass it to me
> Before, by some wayside,
> A potter uses your clay and mine for just such a jug.

Every time Richard had passed his large neighbour's desk, he was gazing – transfixed – at the message on his screen. Richard could only suppose it had done wonders for his colleague's self-esteem.

On Thursday there were two thoughts for the day, transmitted every two hours, alternately:

> Before you are taken in ambush
> Order the rose-hued wine to be fetched
> You're not gold, you silly fool,
> To be buried in the ground and then brought out again.
>
> How long will you chatter about the five senses and the four elements?
> What matters if the puzzles be one or a hundred thousand?
> We are dust, strum the harp, boy,
> We are air, boy, bring out the wine.

That day both neighbours accepted Richard's invitation to lunch.

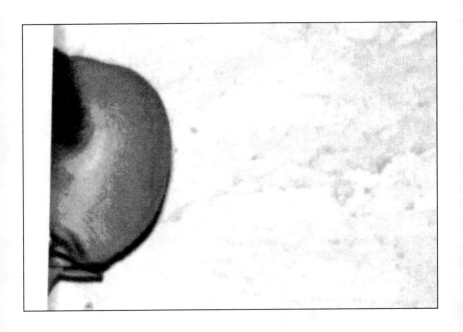

Richard is whispering now. I crouch closer. He wants his thought for the day to be more widely disseminated. Is Mark's accountancy firm on the Internet? I don't know. Can I find out? I suppose I...

'WE ARE NOT ON THE INTERNET,' declares Mark, unambiguously enough.

Mark looks worried. He's sitting in the fifth cubicle with his shoulders hunched protectively around his ears and his right hand tensely gripping his left wrist. Both thumbs rub up and down adjoining flesh to the same rhythm. Bringing some kind of comfort? Mark catches my eye and beckons me forward as he shuffles into the cubicle corner.

Earnestly, Mark talks to me about his office (he is a partner in a firm of chartered accountants), but the picture I'm getting is hazy. Losing patience with my confusion, Mark pulls a notebook from his pocket and begins to draw a diagram. Finished, he holds it at arm's length and scrutinizes his handiwork for several seconds before handing it over to me.

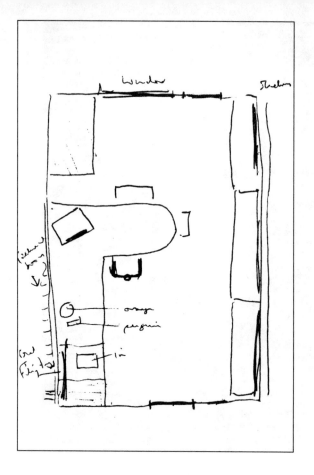

The emphasized feature in the middle of the room is Mark
sitting at his L-shaped desk; the box on the desk is Mark's computer; and the words noted in Mark's crabbed handwriting are
'window', 'shelves', 'technical books', 'orange', 'penguin', 'out
filing tray' and 'in'.

Orange? Penguin?... Mark nods. These are kept on his desk
to accompany morning coffee (Penguin) and afternoon tea
(orange). I nod, slowly. Pleased to see that I seem to be getting
the gist of his office, Mark retrieves the notebook and makes
additions to his diagram which he talks me through.

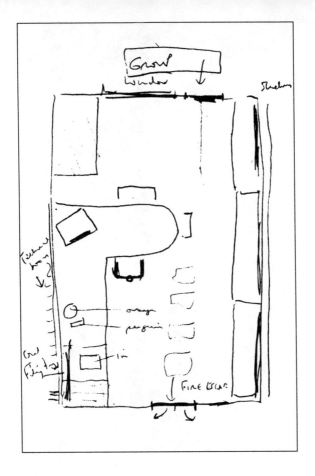

There are always piles of files on the floor of Mark's room, blocking the fire escape that serves Mark's group. As soon as the fire bell rings, he must move the files on to his desk or on to the filing cabinets to protect them from the rush through his room. On Monday the bell went mid-coffee break. Mark had to bolt his Penguin and, in some sort of nervous reaction, has rushed his coffee break each day since. A state of affairs that has had a negative effect on his efficiency.

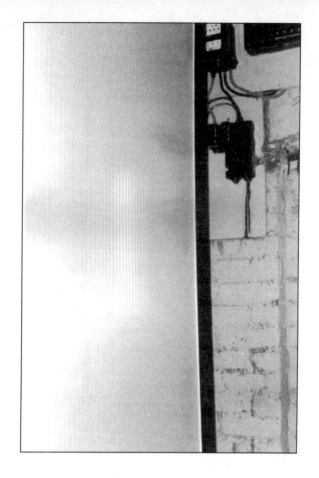

I look away from the diagram, trying to get a perspective. I suppose the serious point Mark's making is that in a day spent disciplining and driving his mind, periods of self-nurture – pampering, even – are essential. Mark nods emphatically, scribbling down another diagram. 'This is the right wall of my office,' he tells me.

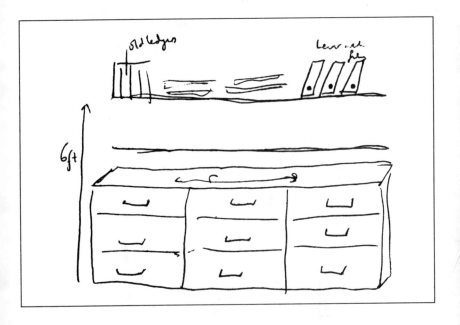

The massive set of steel drawers is so bulky that Mark would-
n't be able to access the lever-arch files on the shelf above but
for the holes in their spines. Anyway, it is the bottom-left-hand
drawer that Mark asks me to take particular note of. For two reasons. But to explain why, he needs to refer to his plan diagram.

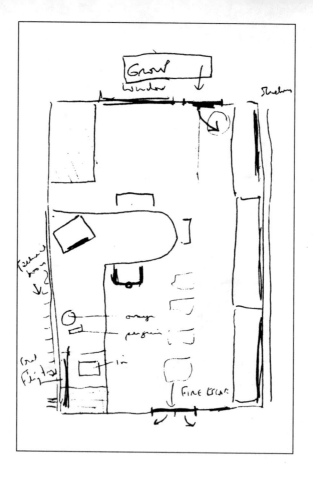

Correspondence files that Mark constantly refers to are kept in that drawer. Regularly someone will throw open the room's door, flattening Mark against the wall. It feels strange, Mark tells me, being confined to a small proportion of his whole office, albeit fleetingly.

The second thing about this drawer is that it slides open by itself on occasions, like if Mark slams the door as he goes out. When this happens Mark can't open the door far enough to get back into his office. Not until he's gone downstairs, obtained a broom from the kitchen and manipulated the head of that so as to slide shut the offending drawer.

I feel a grip on the big toe of my right foot. I'd imagined it was just the top of Richard's head and the end of ▮▮▮▮▮ at were in cubicle four, but that can no longer be the case. Has Richard crawled right the way into the cubicle so as to be able to get his teeth around the toe of my shoe? Possibly. I decide to wait for further developments.

Another squeeze, harder this time and made by hand, I think. 'What is it, Richard?' Richard has some advice for Mark. 'Let's hear it, then,' says Mark, in that peremptory way of his when intimidated. Richard's advice: as soon as Mark hears the fire bell ringing he should open the bottom drawer so that the rest of his group can't charge through his room and upset the very important papers. Mark can then take his time in rearranging his office and only when that's done to his satisfaction need he close the drawer, hide in the corner and allow the fire drill to proceed. Disdainfully, Mark informs Richard that he thought of this long ago.

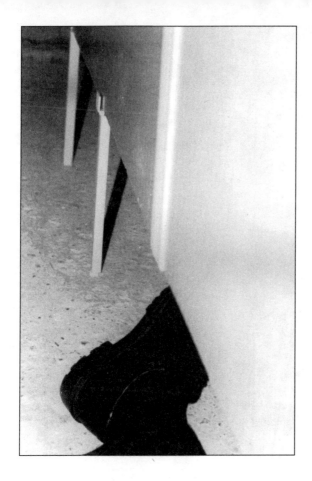

Unfortunately, the staff have got wise to the situation. According to Mark, within seconds of the fire bell sounding, colleagues rush through his room brandishing croquet mallets, pitchforks, vacuum-cleaner attachments, shoes jammed on to sticks, any one of which could have closed the drawer in an instant...

Silence and stillness. I let both continue. I realize how peaceful it has become in the basement gallery now that the hordes that Mark conjured up have passed away. I sit there enjoying the ambience.

Mark has stood up: silently.

Silence. 'Are you there, Richard?'

No answer. I decide to investigate.

Cubicle four is empty. Cubicle three is not empty. Richard is asleep on his feet, or in some sort of coma. I don't disturb him.

Cubicle two is empty. Cubicle one is not empty. Joanna's breathing is deep and even. The mumbling I can hear is not emanating from this cubicle but from the right. I retrace my steps.

Silence from cubicle three, but I enter it anyway and tap Richard on the shoulder. You see, I don't think Richard told me his thought for today and I'm suddenly curious. He is deeply asleep though. More mumbling; not from here, from further right. I step back.

Mark is talking in his coma. He's safe, he tells me. Three times safe in his office. He is in the drawer; he is in the draw-er which is locked; he is in the drawer which is locked, camou-flaged by orange peel and Penguin wrappers.

I retreat.

'The moron's going. He can't get into the drawer. How can he get into the drawer when I've got the key here in my pocket?'

I try not to take these ravings personally.

But I do need my own space. I'm not comfortable in cubicle four, between Mark and Richard. But cubicle two feels all right – next door to Joanna. I'm also next door to Richard, but I mustn't dwell on that side of the equation if I want to fall asleep. Do I want to fall asleep? I suppose everyone falls asleep sooner or later. But I prefer... to think... I prefer... I prefer...

I open my eyes. How long have I been power-napping? I don't know. Who has invaded my personal space only to map out and acknowledge it? I don't know but I can find out.

Cubicle five. Underneath a yellow Post-it sticker there's another:

> Before the world forgets your name,
> Drink wine – it drives sorrow from the heart
> And before your limbs fall away joint by joint
> Unwind the beauty's tresses, ringlet by ringlet.

I am on for this party. On for it in a big way.

Cubicle four. FIRE ESCAPE to the right. But it is PARTY ESCAPE
I'm looking for.

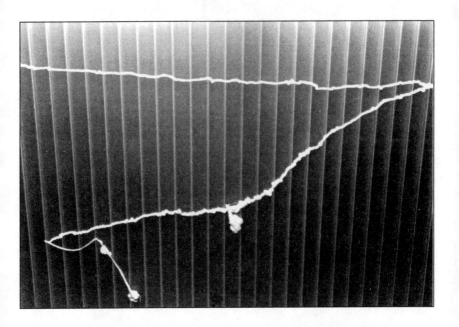

Cubicle three. A solitary zigzag decoration. Richard's pre-party warming-up exercise? Underneath is another Post-it:

> Drink wine, this is life eternal,
> This, all that youth will give you,
> It is the season for wine, roses and friends drinking together,
> Be happy for this moment – it is all life is.

If ever anyone was up for a party, that's me. That's me *now*. That's me walking past cubicle two towards...

Looks like the party's been and gone. Two bottles of wine between the three of them – the pigs. Actually, there's still a glassful left of the dry Portuguese white, so I take a glug out of that. I look round the cubicle; I'd say that a pretty good time had been had. I finish off the white and check the Rioja, but it's dead all right.

Thinking of Mark, Richard and Joanna together reminds me of when the four of us worked for the same accountancy firm. Joanna was the personnel officer, Mark and I were bright new recruits, and Richard was so hopeless with figures that he was taken out of active service. He was a popular figure about the office due to his irrepressible good nature, however. So Joanna was able to find him an administrative job with the firm. Richard cleaned the gents', partners' and ladies' toilets for years. That's how I remember it, anyway.

Joanna's room in the old offices. A lot of well-watered plants spread around it. The top of her desk covered by a sheet of glass; in between the glass and desktop an array of postcards – reproductions of well-known works of art. There had been something sad but hopeful about the little plants in their pots, the little cards behind the glass and the woman who was doing what she could to preserve her dignity and values in a place where an absence of such was the general rule.

Recently Joanna told me how she'd always disliked going into the group room where Mark and I worked. Amidst the office paraphernalia there was a single decoration, a poster on the wall showing the rear view of a tall, blonde, young woman holding a tennis racquet. Her free hand lifting her skimpy skirt to reveal much of her bare bottom. Standing in the middle of the room, delivering her message to whomever, Joanna had to fight off the impression she was being stripped naked by the eyes of every young male in the room.

Mark still works there. How can he stand it? Things have improved, apparently. More women have been recruited (a trend begun by Joanna) and they have had a civilizing influence. Mark's generation has risen to power and theirs is a more enlightened management. Of course, no office could be an ideal human environment, Mark knew that. Just as he knew what he was doing when he produced the sketches and the anecdote for me earlier. Thanks, Mark, I will try not to abuse your generosity.

More wine, please.

Richard's balloon could be hiding a secret supply but it doesn't look like it. I kick the balloon and it ricochets from cubicle to knee to cubicle to hip and out of the corner. Who can resist balloons? – Not me. Kicking, catching, hitting, kissing them. I kiss all the balloons in turn.

I still can't believe they didn't leave me any wine. Well, they did leave me wine, but that was never going to be enough. Who can resist balloons? – Not me. Kicking the big one in the teeth, squeezing another underneath cubicle edge until it bursts – BANG!

There is a black felt-tip on the floor. I pick it up and try it out on the party wall:

WHO CAN RESIST BALLOONS? - NOT ME. BURSTING THE LITTLE ONES WITH EASE, KICKING THE BIG ONE ABOUT THE CUBICLE UNTIL IT TRIES TO ESCAPE OVER THE TOP OF THE BACK WALL. NO CHANCE. KICKING IT ABOUT AGAIN UNTIL IT TRIES TO ESCAPE UNDER THE PARTY WALL. NO CHANCE. BUT LET IT STAY THERE.

WHO CAN RESIST PHOTOGRAPHS? - NOT ME. I CAN'T WAIT TO GET HOME AND SEE HOW TODAY'S HAVE TURNED OUT. ONE IN PARTICULAR I HAVE HIGH HOPES FOR. I'LL BE ON TENTERHOOKS UNTIL IT'S SAFELY DEVELOPED.

PARTY ON RICHARD, JOANNA, MARK.

Party on, Richard...

267

WHAT DID THE SPIDER SAY TO THE FLY?

ET IN ARCADIA RICHARD

Mr D McLaren
51 Sunderland Road
Forest Hill
London SE23 2PS

Dear Duncan

Vying with each other for obscurity, here is a Xerox copy (originals available, if required) of my latest acquisition, an AEC Mandator 16 ton lorry. Thanks for Joanna' s latest exhibition postcard.

Anyway see what creative ideas you can place around this.

See you soon.

Yours sincerely,

Richard Butter

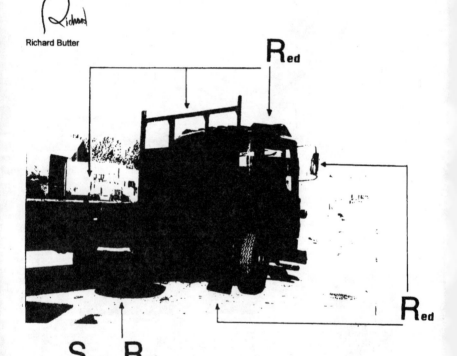

Imagine Richard is going for it

Duncan McLaren
51 Sunderland Road
London SE23 2PS

Tel. 0181 291 6979

Mabel McLaren

5 December, 1997

Dear Mum,

My book on contemporary art, PERSONAL DELIVERY, will be
published next year by Quartet Books. May I reproduce the photos
you took of John and me feeding the seagulls on the ferry to
Ireland in 1966? Dad has read the chapter after which the photos
will appear. He has seen how I have mildly adulterated the
photos, and I know he had a problem with the way I've spelt
'pidgeons'. So by all means consult with him over this question
of permission.

Quartet's production schedule means I need to know by Christmas.
If it simplifies things, please complete the permission request
below and return this letter to me using the SAE.

Love and kisses,

~Juc.

Permission given/~~not given~~. *(delete as applicable)*

Signature and date. *M̶ H̶ M̶c̶ L̶a̶r̶e̶n̶* .   *13/12/97*

ACKNOWLEDGEMENTS

Thanks to artists and galleries who gave me permission to reproduce photographs of their work.

Thanks to artists and everyone else who gave me permission to reproduce correspondence.

Thanks to Richard and Mark for allowing me to take liberties.

Thanks to editors, artists, bus drivers, friends, gallerists, literary agents, landscape gardeners and tattooists who returned my questionnaire – especially Jeremy.

Thanks to Quartet for taking a risk.

Thanks to Jon at Namara for all his expertise.

Thanks most of all to Joanna.

Artists whose work is featured:

Richard Long; Hadrian Pigott, Kerry Stewart
Tilda Swinton and Cornelia Parker
Bob and Roberta Smith
Louisa MacIver and Karen F
Jo Bennett
Milo Garcia
Dalziel and Scullion
Bob and Roberta Smith
Bob and Roberta Smith
Sean Landers
Douglas Gordon
Matthew Higgs and Peter Doig
Edward Lipski; Nicky Hirst
Jeff Wall
Olivier Zabat
Tim Hutchinson, James Young, Dave Willshaw, Jason Coburn
Tracey Emin
David Shrigley
Ross Sinclair
David Shrigley; Bob and Roberta Smith
Bill Viola
Cornelia Parker
Richard Wilson
Carl von Weiler
Jo Bennett, Simon Marshall, Kate Carrick, Nick Symes,
    Tony Peakall, Rose Smith, Alex Schady,
    Steve Thompson, Rochelle Fry, Jon Wright
Jo Bennett